Folens
History in Action 6

Author:
Karen Cooksey

Acknowledgements

The author and publisher would like to thank the following for permission to reproduce the following copyright material:

p.12	Courtesy of the British Empire and Commonwealth Museum – www.empiremuseum.co.uk
p.15	© S. Sassoon/Robert Harding Picture Library.
pp.16 & 19	Information taken from *The Indus Valley* (National Curriculum History: Key Stage 2) by Ilona Aronovsky and Umaya Aafjes-Sinnadurai, published by the Commonwealth Institute.
p.27	Extract taken from *Excavations at Aztec Peasant Sites* by Michael E. Smith www.albany.edu/~mesmith/rural.html
p.30	Map based on findings by Michael E. Smith, taken from *Yautepec, an Aztec City* www.albany.edu/~mesmith/yaucity.html
p.66	Quotes written by David Ashton. For more about childhood memories of John Lennon see www.beatlesireland.utvinternet.com
p.73	The Advertising Archive Ltd.
p.77	'Death of a Beatle' from Newsweek magazine, 22 December 1980
pp.77 & 79	'The night Lennon died' from BBC News at www.bbcnews.com

Commissioning editor: Zoë Nichols
Editor: Caroline Marmo
Layout artist: Suzanne Ward
Illustrations: Catherine Ward (SGA Illustration and Design)
Cover design: Philippa Jarvis
Cover image: © Werner Forman/CORBIS

First published 2005 by Folens Limited.

British Library Cataloguing in Publication Data. A catalogue record for this publication is available from the British Library.

ISBN 1 84303 762 9

Contents

Introduction

Folens History in Action meets the requirements for the National Curriculum in England and Wales, and is compatible with the schemes of work published in England by the Qualifications and Curriculum Authority (QCA). It will work best when combined with a range of history resources such as books, photos, videos, artefacts and, for some topics, interviews with visitors.

Aims of Folens History in Action

The overall aim of the book is that children should: develop knowledge and understanding of significant periods, people and events in history; and learn to interpret historical evidence and understand that knowledge about history is subject to interpretation.

The aim of individual activities is to provide opportunities for children to engage with the subject matter and process it in some way, such as matching, sequencing, using information to draw, write a specific form of text, or label a diagram. Children's thinking skills will develop better if they are allowed to verbalise their thought processes in pairs or small groups; most of the activities are designed to be used in this way.

The Structure of Folens History in Action

The book is divided into five units, each covering one of the history topics suitable for Years 5 and 6, as defined by the schemes of work. It is expected that teachers will choose either the **Indus Valley Civilisation** or the **Aztec Civilisation** for one term's work. The **Ancient Greek Civilisation** provides a term's work and could be combined with the unit on **Greek Legacy**. The final unit, **John Lennon**, would be most suitable for the shortest of the three terms.

Activities in the units on the ancient civilisations in the Indus Valley and Mexico (Aztecs) put the children in the place of the archaeologist or historian who is making interpretations and deductions. The focus is on how we know about the everyday life of the people. The two units on Ancient Greece are more concerned with understanding aspects of the culture or significant events and appreciating the connections to modern times. Finally, John Lennon is an example of a person in the recent past who has had an influence on his times; the activities will help children to understand the reasons and assess the consequences of this.

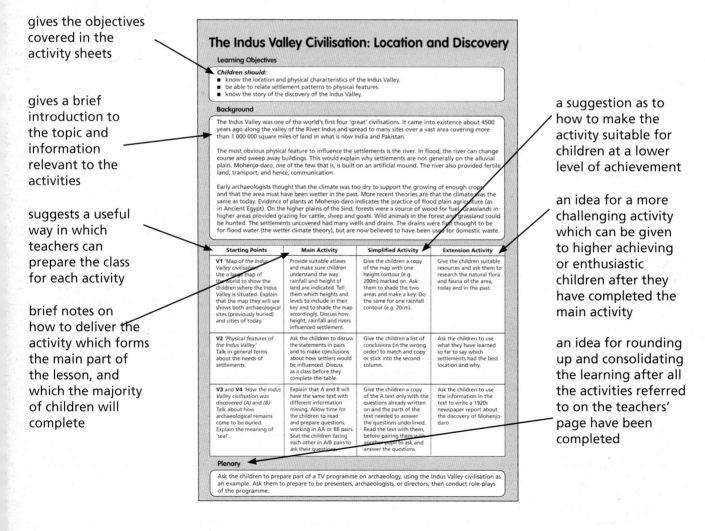

gives the objectives covered in the activity sheets

gives a brief introduction to the topic and information relevant to the activities

suggests a useful way in which teachers can prepare the class for each activity

brief notes on how to deliver the activity which forms the main part of the lesson, and which the majority of children will complete

a suggestion as to how to make the activity suitable for children at a lower level of achievement

an idea for a more challenging activity which can be given to higher achieving or enthusiastic children after they have completed the main activity

an idea for rounding up and consolidating the learning after all the activities referred to on the teachers' page have been completed

The Indus Valley Civilisation: Location and Discovery

Learning Objectives

Children should:
- know the location and physical characteristics of the Indus Valley.
- be able to relate settlement patterns to physical features.
- know the story of the discovery of the Indus Valley.

Background

The Indus Valley was one of the world's first four 'great' civilisations. It came into existence about 4500 years ago along the valley of the River Indus and spread to many sites over a vast area covering more than 1 000 000 square miles of land in what is now India and Pakistan.

The most obvious physical feature to influence the settlements is the river. In flood, the river can change course and sweep away buildings. This would explain why settlements are not generally on the alluvial plain. Mohenjo-daro, one of the few that is, is built on an artificial mound. The river also provided fertile land, transport, and hence, communication.

Early archaeologists thought that the climate was too dry to support the growing of enough crops, and that the area must have been wetter in the past. More recent theories are that the climate was the same as today. Evidence of plants at Mohenjo-daro indicates the practice of flood plain agriculture (as in Ancient Egypt). On the higher plains of the Sind, forests were a source of wood for fuel. Grasslands in higher areas provided grazing for cattle, sheep and goats. Wild animals in the forest and grassland could be hunted. The settlements uncovered had many wells and drains. The drains were first thought to be for flood water (the wetter climate theory), but are now believed to have been used for domestic waste.

Starting Points	Main Activity	Simplified Activity	Extension Activity
V1 *'Map of the Indus Valley civilisation'* Use a large map of the world to show the children where the Indus Valley is situated. Explain that the map they will see shows both archaeological sites (previously buried) and cities of today.	Provide suitable atlases and make sure children understand the way rainfall and height of land are indicated. Tell them which heights and levels to include in their key and to shade the map accordingly. Discuss how height, rainfall and rivers influenced settlement.	Give the children a copy of the map with one height contour (e.g. 200m) marked on. Ask them to shade the two areas and make a key. Do the same for one rainfall contour (e.g. 20cm).	Give the children suitable resources and ask them to research the natural flora and fauna of the area, today and in the past.
V2 *'Physical features of the Indus Valley'* Talk in general terms about the needs of settlements.	Ask the children to discuss the statements in pairs and to make conclusions about how settlers would be influenced. Discuss as a class before they complete the table.	Give the children a list of conclusions (in the wrong order) to match and copy or stick into the second column.	Ask the children to use what they have learned so far to say which settlements had the best location and why.
V3 and **V4** *'How the Indus Valley civilisation was discovered (A) and (B)'* Talk about how archaeological remains come to be buried. Explain the meaning of 'seal'.	Explain that A and B will have the same text with different information missing. Allow time for the children to read and prepare questions, working in AA or BB pairs. Seat the children facing each other in A/B pairs to ask their questions.	Give the children a copy of the A text only with the questions already written on and the parts of the text needed to answer the questions underlined. Read the text with them, before pairing them with another pupil to ask and answer the questions.	Ask the children to use the information in the text to write a 1920s newspaper report about the discovery of Mohenjo-daro.

Plenary

Ask the children to prepare part of a TV programme on archaeology, using the Indus Valley civilisation as an example. Ask them to prepare to be presenters, archaeologists, or directors, then conduct role-plays of the programme.

Map of the Indus Valley civilisation

- Use an atlas to find out about the natural features of the Indus Valley. Make a key to show the height of the land and the amount of rainfall.

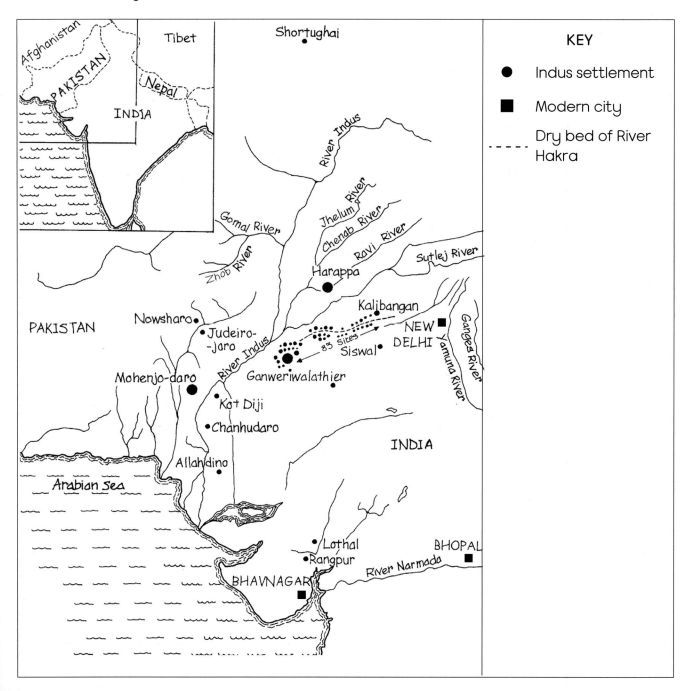

KEY

● Indus settlement

■ Modern city

- - - - - Dry bed of River Hakra

- Describe any connection you can see between where most settlements are located and the physical features of the area.

_____

_____

_____

_____

_____

Physical features of the Indus Valley

Archaeologists can make theories about how the Ancient Indus Valley people lived by looking at the climate and the natural features. What would these things mean for the early inhabitants of the Indus Valley? Complete the right-hand boxes.

Use these words:

building   timber   water   wells   hunting   transport

fishing   growing crops   grazing

Physical features	Affect on the Ancient Indus Valley people
The Indus River floods every year. It can cause a lot of damage. The time, the strength and the location of the floods are different every year.	They could not build cities next to the rivers.
When the river floods it leaves behind a rich alluvial soil. It is very fertile.	
The area occupied by the settlements is arid or semi-arid (low rainfall).	
There are grasslands in the higher areas.	
The river system can be navigated.	
In dry areas it is possible to dig down to underground water.	
There are forests on some of the higher areas.	
Animals that lived in forested area and grasslands probably included: elephant, rhinoceros, zebra, buffalo, tiger, hog, deer, cobra and crocodile.	

How the Indus Valley civilisation was discovered (A)

- Read the text and write questions to get the missing information from your partner. Be ready to answer your partner's questions.

An English man called Charles Masson was travelling through India (the part that is now Pakistan) in the year _____. Near the village of Harappa he was shown a ruined brick castle with very high walls and towers, built on a hill. He wrote about what he had seen.

Some years later, the bricks of the castle were used to _____ . In 1853, when an archaeologist called Sir Alexander Cunningham examined the ruins, the castle had gone. Instead he found a huge mound of walls and rubble. He thought they must be from a very old city. He found a little polished stone square, carved with an _____ . It was a seal – for pressing into a softer material, like clay. He didn't think it could be from India or Pakistan. In those days, historians thought that the oldest cities in India were from 500BC.

An archaeologist called _____ began excavating at the site in the year 1921. He found more seals at the bottom of a trench. Digging down, he found seven or eight layers of walls and houses. He thought the ruins belonged to a city that was very big and about 2500 years old.

Four hundred miles away another archaeologist excavated a ruined brick mound near the Indus River. The local people called it _____ . He found a seal the same as the one at Harappa. This meant that the two cities could belong to the same civilisation, and that it was very big. It was an exciting discovery.

Over the next 15 years the cities at Mohenjo-daro and Harappa were further excavated; buildings, streets and objects were discovered. Since then thousands of small settlements and several more larger cities have been discovered around the Indus and the rivers leading into it. They all have buildings, objects and seals that show they belong to the same civilisation as the cities at Mohenjo-daro and Harappa. Now we know that the Indus Valley people were some of the first in the world to _____ .

Questions:

_____

_____

_____

_____

_____

How the Indus Valley civilisation was discovered (B)

- Read the text and write questions to get the missing information from your partner. Be ready to answer your partner's questions

An English man called _____ was travelling through India (the part that is now Pakistan) in the year 1826. Near the village of Harappa he was shown a _____ , built on a hill. He wrote about what he had seen.

Some years later, the bricks of the castle were used to lay railway tracks. In 1853, when an archaeologist called Sir Alexander Cunningham examined the ruins, the castle had gone. Instead he found a _____ .
He thought they must be from a very old city. He found a little polished stone square, carved with an animal picture and some kind of picture writing. It was a seal – for pressing into a softer material, like clay. He didn't think it could be from India or Pakistan. In those days, historians thought that the oldest cities in India were from _____ BC.

An archaeologist called Daya Ram Sahni began excavating at the site in the year 1921. He found more seals at the bottom of a trench. Digging down, he found seven or eight layers of walls and houses. He thought the ruins belonged to a city that was very big and about _____ years old.

Four hundred miles away another archaeologist excavated a ruined brick mound near the Indus River. The local people called it Mohenjo-daro (Mound of the Dead). He found a seal the same as the one at Harappa. This meant that the two cities could belong to the same civilisation, and that it was very big. It was an exciting discovery.

Over the next 15 years the cities at Mohenjo-daro and Harappa were further excavated; buildings, streets and objects were discovered. Since then thousands of small settlements and several more _____ have been discovered around the Indus and the rivers leading into it. They all have buildings, objects and seals that show they belong to the same civilisation as the cities at Mohenjo-daro and Harappa. Now we know that the Indus Valley people were some of the first in the world to live in cities.

Questions:

_____

_____

_____

_____

_____

Mohenjo-daro

Learning Objectives

Children should:
- relate the age of the Indus Valley civilisation to other known ancient civilisations.
- appreciate the size and aspects of remains at Mohenjo-daro as evidence of advanced culture.

Background

The Indus Valley civilisation lasted from about 2500BC to 1500BC. Before this period there is evidence of some cultivation of the land and grazing of animals (pastoralism), but no established settlements. From 2500BC, for 200 to 300 years there is evidence that farmers were moving to the alluvial plains, and villages were established. The mature period of civilisation (cities and advanced technology) was from 2300BC to 1700BC. For the next 200 years the society was in decline.

Evidence that indicates a 'mature' or advance Indus settlement includes: a citadel complex with high walls, next to a lower residential area; thick red pottery; large bricks in regular size – 4:2:1; seals with script and animal motifs; models with wheels; copper or bronze spears; barbed fish hooks; regular flat axes; and shell bangles.

The remains of Mohenjo-daro cover about 1.5 square kilometres and recent estimates of the original population are around 150 000. Only 10 per cent of the site has been excavated; water has prevented further work. Deposits of salty soil and mud have raised the plain by nine metres since the city was built.

Starting Points	Main Activity	Simplified Activity	Extension Activity
V5 *'Timeline for the Indus Valley civilisation'* Talk about the way archaeological evidence is found in layers. Discuss the dates of other ancient civilisations the class has studied.	Point out that the diagram corresponds to layers underground, and that advanced technology enables more objects to be found. For the early period tell them to write what wouldn't be found.	Give them a list of objects and ask them to draw the objects in either the middle and top layer, or the top layer only on the second task.	Give the children suitable resources and ask them to research the actual signs that archaeologists use to identify advanced Indus Valley civilisation. Ask them to report to the class.
V6 *'The size of Mohenjo-daro'* Demonstrate and practise using a scale to work out real distances. Measure your classroom and the school hall in preparation for the second activity.	Ask the children to work in pairs to calculate the distances. Ask individuals to explain their calculations. Provide a suitable map of a nearby urban area and population figures.	Give the children extra instructions, either verbal or written, to help them to calculate the distances e.g. *multiply by x to get the number of metres.*	Ask the children to list any other clues that archaeologists could use to work out the population of an ancient city. (Farmed area, size of store, artefacts to help work out how many people lived in a house and so on.)
V7 *'Building the city'* Talk about the building of a city or settlement: features that would have to be collectively planned, and those that would not.	Read the evidence with the class and discuss why advanced technology would be needed. Ask them to work individually or in pairs to complete the second part of the activity.	Begin as for the main activity. Ask the children to underline the relevant jobs and write a sentence about what each person would do.	Show the children photographs of buildings at Mohenjo-daro. Ask them to draw an imaginary scene of construction work in progress at the city. Discuss dress and equipment used.

Plenary

Divide the board in half and write the titles 'fact' and 'belief'. Recall with the children what they have learned so far about Mohenjo-daro. Ask them which heading each contribution should go under and compile a list.

Timeline for the Indus Valley civilisation

- Read the information below about the different stages of the Indus Valley civilisation.
  Use a different colour to mark each stage accurately on the timeline.

AD2000

AD1000

Common
Era 1

1000BC

2000BC

3000BC

Decline
1700BC–1500BC
People abandoned the cities.
Decline of the Indus Valley civilisation.

Advanced Stage
2200BC–1700BC
People lived in cities.
Technology was more advanced.

Middle Stage
2500BC–2200BC
Farmers moved to the alluvial plains of the Indus River.
People lived in villages.

Early Stage
3300BC–2500BC
People cultivated the land and grazed animals.
They moved from place to place.

- In each box, draw and label some archaeological
  evidence that could be found from the different
  stages.

Advanced

Middle

Early

- Find out about other ancient civilisations and mark
  these on the timeline.

The size of Mohenjo-daro

● Use the scale to find out these distances:

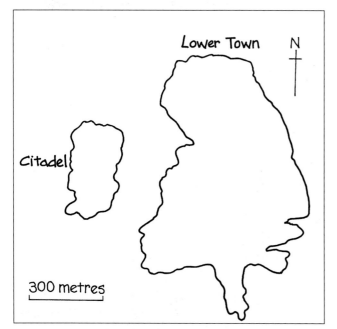

The citadel, north to south. _____

The citadel, east to west. _____

The Lower Town, north to south._____

The Lower Town, east to west. _____

The shortest distance between the Citadel

and the Lower Town. _____

Draw a grid over the plan and work out, approximately, the total surface area.

Compare this to a densely populated area near you. How many people live in that area?

_____

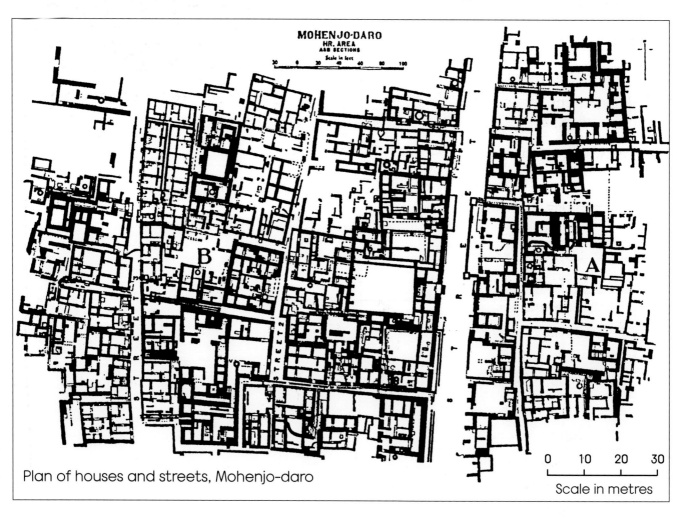

Plan of houses and streets, Mohenjo-daro

● Measure the size of the largest buildings. Compare them to the size of your classroom and school hall. Use these measurements to make a guess at how many people could live in this area.

_____

Building the city

Evidence of the advanced technology and engineering used at Mohenjo-daro.

◆ The city is built on artificial mounds.

◆ All the main streets are built in a north-south direction.

◆ The streets have drains running down them.

◆ The houses have clay drain pipes in the walls.

◆ There are at least 600 wells, each up to 10 metres deep.

◆ All of the bricks are built to the same ratio: 4 units long, 2 units wide, 1 unit high.

Historians believe that the following jobs were done in the city. Underline those needed for planning and building.

Architects

Brick makers

Carpenters

Engineers (building experts)

Farmers

House builders

Jewellers

Law keepers

Metal makers

Merchants

Priests/religious leaders

Potters

Rulers

Sculptors

Seal makers

Soldiers

Spinners, weavers and dyers

Well builders

Street cleaners

● At least one archaeologist, Michael Jansen, thinks that Mohenjo-daro was a new town, like Milton Keynes, planned and built in one go. Use the information about the city to write a list of what was done, in the right order.

1. *The planners and rulers chose a good site for the city.*

Looking at Archaeological Evidence in Mohenjo-daro: Buildings

Learning Objectives

Children should:
- understand that different theories can arise from the same archaeological evidence.
- make interpretations based on evidence of buildings and artefacts.

Background

Experts seem to agree that the 'Great Bath' in Mohenjo-daro was used for religious purposes. One theory is that the individual rooms could have been used by priests. It has also been referred to as 'the earliest public water tank in the ancient world'. As yet no similar buildings in other settlements have been found. The shape and watertight bricks and tar seal should give children sufficient clues as to its main purpose.

The Great Granary in the citadel at Mohenjo-daro is a good example of different theories about one building. The first excavations led to the idea that it was a hot air bath. When completely excavated in 1953 it was believed to be a granary that had had a wooden floor, walls and a roof. Later the sockets for wooden beams were deemed too small to be supports for a roof for the whole building. Most recently it was suggested that it was not a granary at all, but could have been used for storing other goods.

The notes on page 16 are from the Commonwealth Institute pack, which also contains useful plans of the areas that have been excavated (see acknowledgements reference on page 2 for more information). The area pictured is a small part of the south of the Lower Town. This area was excavated by archaeologists Hargreaves and Sahni from 1925–27.

Starting Points	Main Activity	Simplified Activity	Extension Activity
V8 *'An important public building'* This activity will only work if children do not already know about the Great Bath. Give an example of the way that different theories arise from evidence. Use the 'Great Granary' at Mohenjo-daro as an example.	Make it clear that any theory is acceptable so long as it uses a) the evidence b) prior knowledge about the Indus Valley civilisation. Allow time for children to discuss in pairs or groups and write theories. Tell them the most popular theory.	Read the evidence with the children. Give them two theories about the building. (It was a public bath. It was a king's palace). Ask them to write sentences to explain why they agree with one theory, but not the other, using the evidence.	Give the children evidence about another Indus Valley civilisation building and ask them to produce a theory.
V9 and **V10** *'Streets and houses (1) and (2)'* Prepare the children for some of the vocabulary used on page 16 (alabaster, limestone, seal).	Allow time for children to study page 16 and answer any questions about the meaning of the notes. Invite some theories and questions before giving them page 17 and asking them to complete the activity.	Give the children a copy of page 16 with only the notes for: house 1, house 3, house 4, room 5, and 6. Ask them to match these to the theories on page 17, and to write some questions of their own.	Ask the children to write a short story based on one of the pieces of evidence, for example, how the man in the courtyard was buried; what happened to the alabaster statue.

Plenary

Ask the children to imagine preparing for an archaeological field trip to Mohenjo-daro. This could take place in groups with children listing equipment, looking at maps, planning known buildings they would like to examine, or new areas where they would like to dig.

An important public building

● Look at the photograph of an important building at Mohenjo-daro and read the information. Write two theories about what this building could be.

◆ The middle area is 11.89m long, 7.1m wide and 2.44m deep.

◆ It has a smooth brick floor and walls, set in a layer of bitumen (tar).

◆ The bricks are fitted tightly together.

◆ At each end there are nine steps and a ledge at the bottom.

◆ There is a large drain in one corner.

◆ Surrounding the middle area there is a low area that had a wooden platform, built on bricks.

◆ Around the platform there were doors or windows and a corridor.

◆ There are eight rooms on the east side, with drains and staircases that went up to another floor or the roof.

◆ In one of the rooms there is a well.

Theory 1	Theory 2
_____	_____
_____	_____
_____	_____
_____	_____
_____	_____
_____	_____
_____	_____
_____	_____
_____	_____

Streets and houses (1)

- Use this sheet with worksheet V10.

The plan shows a small section of the excavated residential area of Mohenjo-daro. The notes describe the buildings and objects that have been found in or near them.

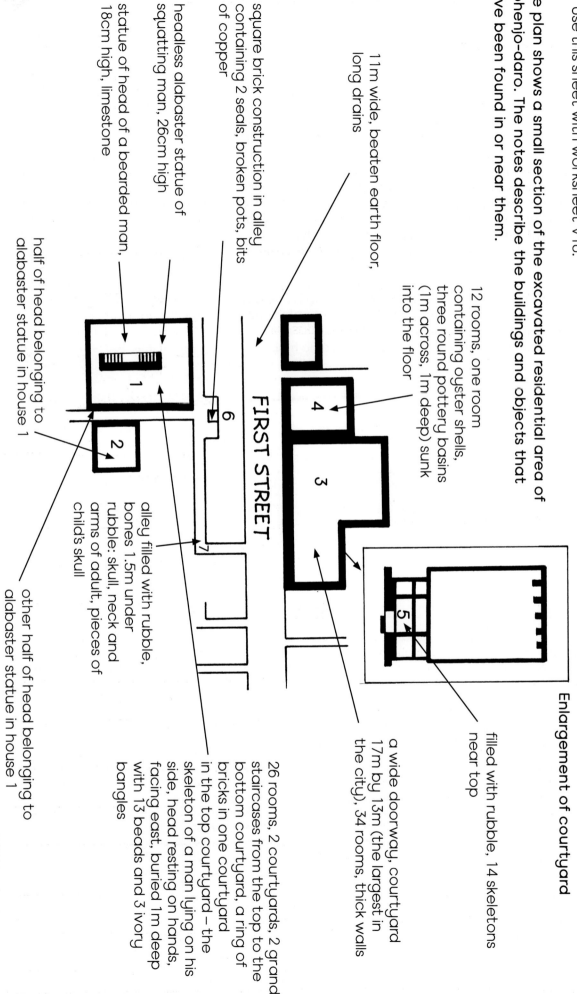

Enlargement of courtyard

12 rooms, one room containing oyster shells, three round pottery basins (1m across, 1m deep) sunk into the floor

11m wide, beaten earth floor, long drains

square brick construction in alley containing 2 seals, broken pots, bits of copper

headless alabaster statue of squatting man, 26cm high

statue of head of a bearded man, 18cm high, limestone

half of head belonging to alabaster statue in house 1

FIRST STREET

alley filled with rubble, bones 1.5m under rubble: skull, neck and arms of adult, pieces of child's skull

other half of head belonging to alabaster statue in house 1

filled with rubble, 14 skeletons near top

a wide doorway, courtyard 17m by 13m (the largest in the city), 34 rooms, thick walls

26 rooms, 2 courtyards, 2 grand staircases from the top to the bottom courtyard, a ring of bricks in one courtyard in the top courtyard – the skeleton of a man lying on his side, head resting on hands, facing east, buried 1m deep with 13 beads and 3 ivory bangles

FOLENS HISTORY IN ACTION 6

Streets and houses (2)

● Look at the plan and notes on worksheet V9.

Here are some of the archaeologists' theories about the buildings. Write the number that each theory applies to.

> ◆ A room in this house could have been used for dyeing cloth. _____
>
> ◆ This building could have been a palace. _____
>
> ◆ This room could have been the guardroom of the palace. _____
>
> ◆ This house must have belonged to important people. _____
>
> ◆ This construction could have been a dustbin. _____

● Write questions about the other evidence uncovered. Write a possible answer for each one.

Questions	My theory
Why was a man buried in house 1?	

Interpreting Evidence: Everyday Life, Trade and Script

Learning Objectives

Children should:
- develop skills of deduction by examining archaeological evidence.
- make deductions by combining sources of evidence.

Background

Objects from Mohenjo-daro pictured on page 19 are presumed to be: a decorated pot with painted goat, whistle shaped like a bird, jewellery, a game, a comb, a cage for an insect, a cup with a handle and a child's drinking cup. Some of them are fairly obvious and others must be best guesses and could be wrong, so it is important not to give the children the idea that there is a right or wrong answer.

The main evidence for trade is the raw materials that must have been imported such as: teak, shell, carnelian, tin, steatite and alabaster. Indus Valley products, on the other hand, do not seem to have been found elsewhere. The standardised system of weights and measures indicates organisation on a large scale and some degree of state intervention. Overland and river routes could have linked to seaports. At Lothal (see map on page 6) there is a large construction that could have been a dock, and another that could have been a warehouse.

In the earliest forms of writing, pictures represented real objects. Later signs were used, sometimes for whole words. Some written forms used homonyms; a sign represented another word with the same sound in the spoken language. All of these required a much greater number of signs and pictures than modern scripts where spoken sound units were represented by one or more symbols. The number of signs (about 450) in the Indus Valley civilisation script, indicate that it is the 'logo-syllabic' type, where signs stand for syllables. However, it has not been deciphered.

Starting Points	Main Activity	Simplified Activity	Extension Activity
V11 *'Objects from Mohenjo-daro'* Discuss the sorts of things we can learn from objects: skills, technology, lifestyle of the makers and users.	Allow time for children to discuss the objects in pairs or groups and to agree on the most likely use. Ask individuals to comment on what they learn and discuss as a class before asking them to record on a separate sheet.	Give the children a list of deductions to match to each picture. (They had potter's wheels. They took a lot of trouble over their appearance.)	Ask the children to choose one aspect of life in Mohenjo-daro, give them suitable resources and ask them to do further research, based on found objects.
V12 *'Trade and transport'* Talk about the way that a picture of life in ancient civilisations has to be built up from many sources.	Ask the children to examine and discuss the evidence in pairs, then ask for feedback and build up a list of deductions on the board.	Ask the children to work with a partner who will read the text for each picture with them and encourage them to think about the implications.	Ask the children to use the deductions to write an imaginative account from the point of view of a trader.
V13 *'Indus Valley civilisation script'* Explain how Champollion deciphered Ancient Egyptian hieroglyphics when he realised that they represented sounds and that homonyms were used.	Explain that the Indus Valley script has not yet been deciphered. Make sure that children understand each task and ask them to work through either individually or in pairs. Discuss how experts might work to decode the script.	Ask the children to complete the first exercise and to think of more examples for 1, 2 and 3. Tell them to omit the second task and study the signs for similarities to real objects.	For children interested in deciphering, give them access to a wider range of samples. The British Museum website for the Indus Valley has information on methods of deciphering. www.ancientindia.co.uk/indus/home_set.html

Plenary

Ask the children to imagine writing a book about the Indus Valley civilisation and to think about what the chapter headings would be. Ask them to remember details and allocate them to the correct chapter. What further research would they do in order to write the book?

Objects from Mohenjo-daro

● Look carefully at these objects. Decide what they are, and what they tell us about the people who made and used them.

made of baked clay
painted picture

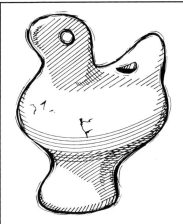

made of baked clay
hole in the tail
makes a sound
when you blow
through it
size: 7.6cm high

beads made of carnelian and other stones
rods between the beads made of copper
size: longest beads, 12cm

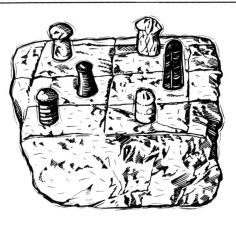

made of stone

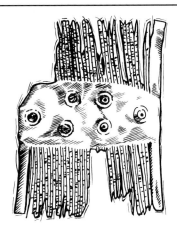

made of ivory
size: 5cm wide

made of baked clay
size: 3.8cm high
clue: breathing holes for something small

made of baked clay
size: 5.5cm high

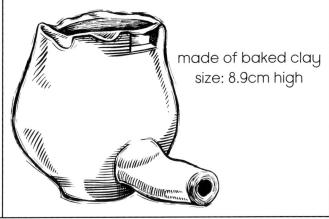

made of baked clay
size: 8.9cm high

Trade and transport

● Look at these four objects and use them to write a theory about how the Indus Valley people traded with other societies.

This tablet shows a flat-bottomed boat. Boats like this are still used on the Indus River today.

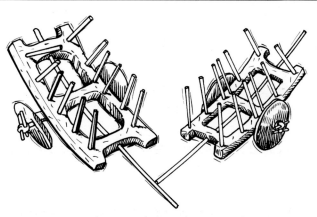

Models of a cart pulled by oxen have been found in many Indus cities. The carts are designed to cope with rough ground. The wheels can easily be taken off for crossing rivers or mud.

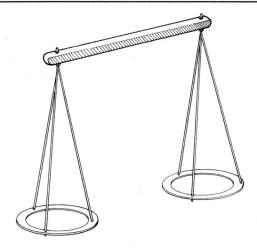

Two small copper plates with three holes were found. They must be the plates for a weighing scale.

These stone weights are found in all the cities. They are always the same size.

How people traded in the Indus Valley civilisation:

Indus Valley civilisation script

The first writing we know about is from 3000BC. Forms of writing have changed over time. Match the examples of writing forms to the descriptions.

a   danger   b   tree

1. An object is represented by a picture. ☐

2. A picture represents an idea or gives a message. ☐

3. A picture represents another word that had the same sound in the language of those people. ☐

c

Um-bre-lla

4. A group of letters represents a sound. [C]

d

Sounds like 'I'

- Which form would need the most symbols?

  _____

- Which forms mean that the reader has to speak the language?

  _____

Here is a theory about the 'fish' sign. Mark each stage with an **F** for fact or a **D** for deduction.

	F / D
The Indus Valley people of 2500BC–500BC probably spoke a 'Dravidian' language. This is the same group as the Tamil language.	_____
The fish sign is very frequently used in the Indus Valley civilisation script.	_____
The Tamil word for fish is 'min'. This is also the word for star.	_____
The fish sign could stand for 'star'.	_____
We know that other societies of that time and region connected gods with stars.	_____
There is a seal from Mohenjo-daro showing a god with a star on either side of his head.	_____
The fish could be a sign for a god of the waters.	_____

- Look at the signs in this seal. What real-life objects could the signs relate to?

The Aztec Civilisation

Learning Objectives

Children should:
- learn how Europeans discovered the Aztec culture and how it was destroyed.
- learn about resources and methods for the rediscovery of the Aztec civilisation.

Background

The city of Tenochtitlan, home of the Mexica, the dominant Aztec group, was founded in 1325 and destroyed by the Spanish in 1521. Spain had conquered and colonised Cuba by 1511 and needed more supplies for the expanding European population. Hernán Cortés was sent to explore, trade, and spread Christianity but he disobeyed orders and set out to conquer, justifying his actions by the barbaric religious practices of the Aztecs and rightly assuming that the wealth acquired would ensure his favour with Moctezuma, the king. The Mexica took supplies from other Aztec groups but did not rule them, hence Cortés was able to gather allies to fight the Mexica.

Moctezuma's initial welcome may have been partly inspired by an Aztec prophesy of a fair-skinned god who would arrive from the east. Cortés took him prisoner to subjugate the people, collecting treasure as ransom. The governor of Cuba sent troops to capture Cortés; Cortés went to subdue them and returned to find that Spanish troops had massacred an unarmed crowd and provoked an uprising. Moctezuma was killed and Cortés' troops went on to completely destroy the city.

Aztecs had a rudimentary writing system but mainly used pictures to keep records, on deerskin and paper. Spanish priests burned the Aztec books and none from before the conquest have survived. However the information that was subsequently gathered and recorded means that the Aztec civilisation is relatively well understood and that archaeological finds have been more easily identified.

Starting Points	Main Activity	Simplified Activity	Extension Activity
A1 *'Timeline of Tenochtitlan'* Explain the Spanish conquest of the Americas in the 1500s and the background to Cortés' expedition. Show the location of Cuba and Mexico on a map.	Ask the children to read the text, marking significant events, then to record the events chronologically on the timeline.	Give the children a list of the main events and dates and ask them to record them on a timeline.	Give the children suitable resources; ask them to read in more detail about the Aztec history, conquest and rediscovery and add more details to the timeline.
A2 *'Written evidence about the Aztecs'* Explain what happened to Aztec books. Show some examples of pages or drawings from the sources on page 24.	Ask the children to read the first paragraph and complete the first row of the table as a class. Ask the children to read and complete the table individually, and compare notes with a partner.	Give the children a copy of the sheet with the 'Purpose of writing' column filled in and the relevant phrases, names and dates to complete the second two rows underlined in the text.	Ask the children to write reasons why each source might, or might not, be reliable. Tell them to consider the motives of the author, how they got their information and the time of writing.
A3 *'Archaeological methods'* Explain what obsidian is; show a picture of an artefact made from obsidian.	Ask the children to cut out the text boxes and discuss them in pairs until they agree on a match. Discuss the methods as a class.	Ask the children to work with a partner who will read the texts with them and help them to discuss each one.	Give the children suitable resources and ask them to find information about the Aztecs that could have been found by each method.

Plenary

As a class, discuss changing attitudes to the Aztec civilisation:
1. The initial attitude of the conquerors.
2. The attitude of the colonists and missionaries who collected information.
3. The attitude of present-day archaeologists and tourists in Mexico.

Timeline of Tenochtitlan

- Read the text and mark the significant events on the timeline.

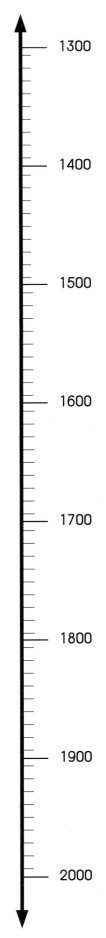

In 1519 a Spanish expedition, led by Hernán Cortés, left Cuba and travelled west. A report the previous year had told them that they would find a wealthy civilisation. They sailed to the coast of the region where the Aztecs lived. The dominant group were the Mexica and their capital was called Tenochtitlan. The Spanish were welcomed by Moctezuma, the king. The huge city amazed them: it was built on a series of islands; the canals and streets were lined with white houses, palaces and temples; the people were dressed in brightly coloured clothes; the markets were full of goods; everywhere was clean and ordered.

One aspect of Aztec life was not so pleasant. They sacrificed their many prisoners and even their own people because they believed the gods demanded it. The walls and floor of the Great Temple were caked with blood! Good relations did not last; the Spanish fought the Mexica in 1521 and with the help of other Aztecs, who did not like them, they conquered and destroyed Tenochtitlan, building another city in its place. The Spanish went on to conquer all of the Aztecs and to rule the country now called Mexico.

The ruins of the Aztec city lay buried under the present Mexico city. Occasionally part of the old city was accidentally uncovered. In 1790 some workmen found a statue of a goddess but they were so terrified by it that they buried it again. In the 1970s builders found the remains of a statue of the Aztec moon goddess. A project began to search for the Great Temple. When it was found archaeologists discovered that it had been rebuilt six times. The first set of walls was dated 1325 by the Aztec calendar.

Written evidence about the Aztecs

● Read about these writings and complete the table.

Viceroy Mendoza requested a book to inform King Carlos V of Spain about his new subjects. Under the supervision of Spanish priests, Aztec scribes illustrated and wrote about the history of their people from 1325 until the conquest. They also described all aspects of the life of the Aztecs from birth to death. The book was finished in 1541 and sent to Spain. French pirates captured the ship and the book went to France instead. Now, it is in the Bodleian Library, Oxford; it is known as the *Codex Mendoza*.

Bernardino de Sahagún was a Spanish missionary who had learned Nahuatl, the Aztec language, and studied the culture of the people. He was such an expert that his superiors asked him to write about the Aztecs for other missionaries and priests, to help them to spread Christianity. Bernardino worked with his fellow friars and with educated Aztecs to produce a manuscript about Aztec culture, including the Aztec beliefs and ideas. The book was finished in 1569 but not published and only used in manuscript form because the Catholic Church did not want to encourage people to read about the old beliefs. It was sent to Spain and eventually published in 1829.

Diego Duran was also a priest who wanted to convert the native people of Mexico to Christianity. He spoke Nahuatl and worked closely with the people. He felt that they said they were Christians but really still kept a lot of their old beliefs and customs. He thought that other priests didn't know enough about Aztec culture to realise this so he wrote three books as a guide to the culture and history of the Aztecs. He interviewed native people about their history and translated what they said. The last book was finished in 1581.

Author(s)	Purpose of writing	Content	Date of completion

FOLENS HISTORY IN ACTION 6

Archaeological methods

- These are some of the methods that archaeologists have used to help them to find out about the Aztecs. Match the method to the type of information found.

Geophysics
Passing an electrical current through the ground. Stone gives a different signal from soil.

A   The age of an organic object.

Osteology
Measuring the size and shape of bones.

B   The age of settlements and objects.

Biology
Examining animal bones.

C   The types of meat people ate.

Pollen analysis
Identifying types of pollen under a microscope.

D   The age, sex and health of a buried person.

Radiocarbon dating
Measuring how much carbon-14 is left in organic matter and, therefore, how old it is.

E   The size of the area covered by a settlement.

Dating obsidian
Measuring the amount of water absorbed into the stone under a microscope. This gives the age of an obsidian tool.

F   The type of crops farmers grew.

Ground survey
Counting the number of objects found per square metre.

G   The location of buried walls.

Everyday Life

Learning Objective

Children should:
- use archaeological and written sources to learn about the everyday life of the Aztecs.

Background

The activities on pages 27–31 are intended to give children opportunities to connect knowledge about the Aztecs to primary and secondary sources, to make some interpretations of their own and to use more than one source. Each activity can lead to further research on the topic.

For page 31, foods eaten in Europe before the conquest are: duck, deer, rabbit, fish and broad beans (all other types of bean were new world discoveries).

Starting Points	Main Activity	Simplified Activity	Extension Activity
A4 *'Aztec village houses'* Talk about the reasons why ordinary dwellings have not been preserved.	Ask the children to discuss the sources in pairs and list all the information that will inform their drawing. Also provide some illustrations of Aztec dress for common people.	Give the children a list of features of Aztec houses (plus illustrations of dress) and ask them to draw a picture.	Give the children suitable resources about the Aztec way of life and ask them to find details to add to their picture.
A5 *'An Aztec craft'* If possible use a wooden spindle and some wool to show how fibres are twisted into a thread.	Ask the children to discuss the pictures in pairs and try to explain the process to each other in detail before writing.	Give the children a frame to structure their writing: *First they used a spindle to … They used a weight to … and a bowl to … .*	Give the children suitable resources. Ask them to investigate another Aztec craft and to report to the class.
A6 *'Farming methods'* Explain that, of the three methods they will study, the first two are still used today by Mexican farmers, whereas the third was discovered by archaeologists.	Allow time for children to study and discuss the diagrams. Ask individuals to explain how the fields would be built before everyone produces a written description.	Give the children questions about the farming methods. *How did they hold the mud in place? Where did the mud come from?* Ask them to look at the pictures and write answers.	Give the children suitable resources. Ask them to find out which crops the Aztecs grew and to report to the class.
A7 *'Yautepec – an Aztec city'* Explain that most Spanish towns were built directly on top of the Aztec ones, but in Yautepec this did not happen.	Read the introductory text together and remind children of methods for calculating area. Provide maps of the local area for comparison. Discuss questions in pairs or as a class.	Give the children specific instructions for calculating the area of the city (by drawing a grid over the map) and for comparing it to a known local area. Omit the questions.	Ask the children to imagine being on the archaeological team and asking permission to search someone's back yard. Ask them to compose a verbal explanation of what they are doing and why.
A8 *'Aztec food'* Show pictures or examples of some of the more unusual foods. Talk about those that were available in Europe before the conquest.	Ask the children to complete the first part of the activity and to discuss the second part with a partner. Ask individuals for their explanation before everyone writes.	Give the children the first part of the activity and ask them to create an illustrated poster about food from the Americas.	Give the children instructions and ingredients for making tortillas!

Plenary

Seat the children in small groups and ask them to plan a display of everything they have learned about the Aztec way of life. Ask a member of each group to describe their plan to the class.

Aztec village houses

In 1985 and 1986 archaeologists Michael Smith and Cynthia Heath–Smith excavated the remains of a rural town, Cuexcomate.

From census records taken after the Spanish conquest:

Average household size: most often 5–6 people, over 8 people in some communities.

Occupants of house: a nuclear family (parents and children) or a joint family (two married couples from the same family and children).

Occupants of a cemithualtin (people who share a yard): most often an extended family (all related), sometimes not related.

Modern Mexican rural dwelling

Excavations at Cuexcomate

Families at Cuexcomate and the nearby single-ward village of Capilco lived in small one-room houses with sun-dried mud brick (adobe) walls and thatched roofs. All that remains of their houses today are the wall foundations and floors that were constructed of stone. When in use, these houses probably looked much like modern adobe peasant houses. Many houses were arranged in small patio groups with two to five houses built around a common open courtyard.

- Use the information to draw a picture of rural Aztec dwellings and people.

An Aztec craft

Archaeologists found pottery, obsidian blades and tools, ceramic figures of people, animals, plants and gods, and lots of spindle weights and bowls for spinning cotton.

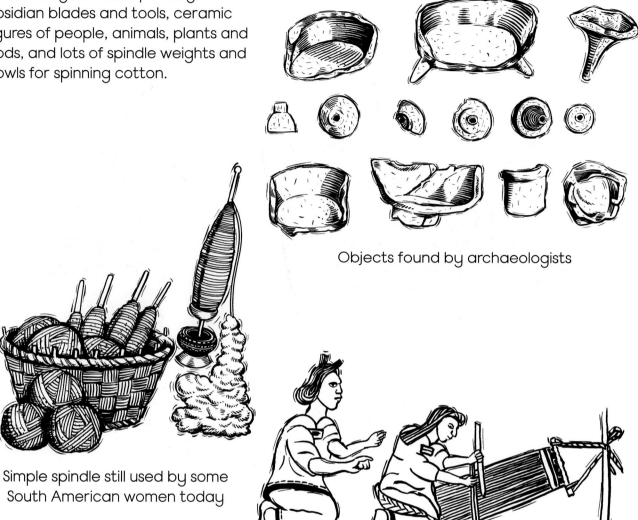

Objects found by archaeologists

Simple spindle still used by some South American women today

Picture from the *Codex Mendoza*

● Use these sources to explain how the Aztecs made cloth.

_____

_____

_____

_____

_____

_____

_____

Farming methods

● Archaeologists discovered three farming methods used by the Aztecs. Look at the diagrams and write a description of each one.

Chinampas (flat, marshy areas)

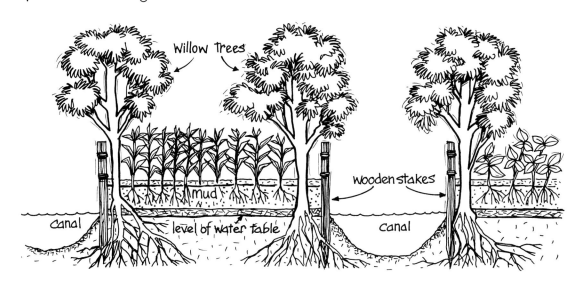

Terraces (dry, hilly areas)

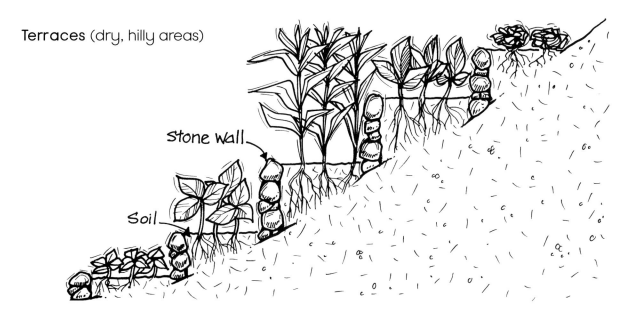

Check Dams (sloping ground with stream)

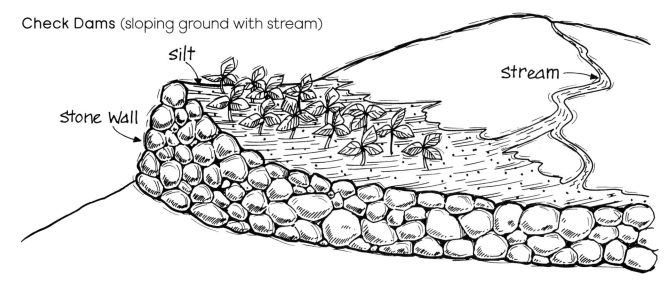

Yautepec – an Aztec city

Archaeologists Michael Smith and Cynthia Heath-Smith were invited by the Mexican government to study the Aztec remains at the city of Yautepec. In 1992, with their team, they carried out a survey, counting the number of artefacts they found in 2 square metres over an area of about 5 square kilometres. Most of the area is covered by fields today, but some is covered by the modern town so they had to knock on doors and ask for permission to search in people's back yards. The artefacts they collected were mainly pieces of pottery and obsidian (black glass-like rock).

This is the map they produced.

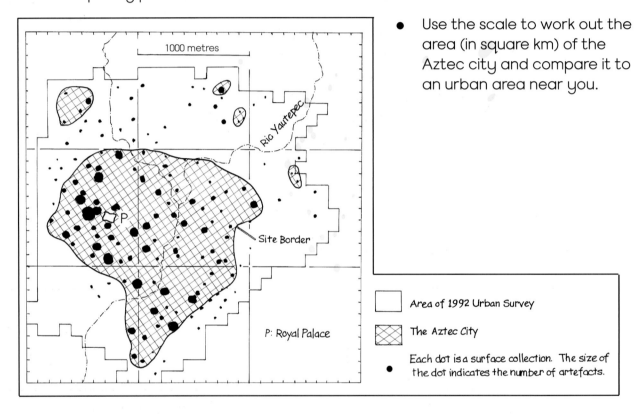

- Use the scale to work out the area (in square km) of the Aztec city and compare it to an urban area near you.

Legend:
- Area of 1992 Urban Survey
- The Aztec City
- Each dot is a surface collection. The size of the dot indicates the number of artefacts.

P: Royal Palace

The archaeologists concluded that the occupation of Yautepec began in the period AD1100–1300. The city grew and was biggest in the period AD1430–1520. Describe the methods they could have used to work this out. (Look again at worksheet A3.)

_____

_____

_____

They found that the city houses were very similar to the rural type houses they had excavated; the main difference was that there were more remains of craft activities in the city houses. Can you think of a reason for this?

_____

_____

_____

Aztec food

Here is a list of things the ordinary Aztecs ate:

At every meal

Maize, usually as tortillas
Beans

Very often

Avocados
Tomatoes
Squash
Chilli peppers
Amaranth seeds
and leaves

In small amounts

Domestic animals: dogs, turkeys,
Muscovy ducks
Hunted animals: deer, rabbit,
iguana, fish
Other sources of protein: insects,
worms, algae from the
surface of lakes

- Underline in red any of the foods that were eaten in Europe at the time of the conquest.
- Underline in blue those foods that are eaten in Europe now.
- What does this tell us about the conquest?

_____

_____

- Explain how each of these things would help historians to know about the Aztec diet.

grinding stones found in houses	bones found in rubbish tips	pictures in the Codex Mendoza and other Aztec writings

Aztec Beliefs

Learning Objectives

Children should:
- learn about the Aztec religion and relate knowledge to primary sources.
- have some understanding of the Aztec counting system.
- learn about the system of tribute.

Background

The Mexica Aztecs believed in gods who demanded human sacrifice, without which there would be no sun or rain. At the top of the Great Temple steps, thousands of victims per year were sliced open, their hearts cut out and offered to Huitzilopochtli, god of war and the sun. Their heads were cut off and their bodies thrown down the steps. The skulls were collected and displayed on racks. Most were prisoners from other groups but some were their own people, specially prepared for the event. There is evidence that other Aztec groups also practised human sacrifice.

Coatlicue was the goddess of life and death. She was portrayed to inspire fear, with sharp claws on her hands and feet, wearing a skirt of snakes and a necklace made from the hearts of her victims. Tlaloc was the god of rain and is portrayed with round bulging eyes and long teeth. Rain was carried up to the sky in jugs by his helpers, according to Aztec belief. The sound of thunder was the smashing of the pots with sticks to release the rain. In the carving, pictured on page 33, the rain appears to be poured.

The Aztecs of Tenochtitlan had two major motives for going to war: capturing prisoners to sacrifice and demanding payment (tribute) to sustain their economy. Their population grew too big to be self-sufficient and they took food, clothing and precious goods from other towns. Not surprisingly, they were unpopular with the other Aztec groups who joined Cortés against them, so ultimately these two practices contributed to their downfall.

Starting Points	Main Activity	Simplified Activity	Extension Activity
A9 *'Aztec religion'* Tell the children about the beliefs of the Aztecs, or provide materials for them to read, before beginning the activity.	Discuss how the objects themselves can convey some of the beliefs (the grandeur of temples, the public nature of death, their fear of the gods), before asking children to write about each picture.	Ask the children to choose one or two of the pictures, explain what it is and the belief connected with it.	Remind the children that a statue of Coatlicue was dug up by workmen in 1790 and reburied because it frightened them. Ask them to write an account from the point of view of one of the workmen.
A10 *'The Aztec calendar'* Talk about how different civilisations have developed different counting systems. Remind the children of any other examples they have studied (Roman).	Present the activity as a puzzle and allow children to work through in pairs to understand the system. Have some numbers already worked out to use as a check of their understanding.	Ask the children to draw the Aztec signs in order down a page, to write numerals 1–20 on the left, and Aztec dots up to 13 then back to 1 on the right.	Give the children suitable resources; ask them to find out how the Aztecs recorded the years and to report to the class.
A11 *'Recording tribute'* Talk about the system of tribute. Introduce the vocabulary for the items of tribute, showing pictures if possible.	Check that the children have worked out the three examples correctly before they proceed to the second half of the activity.	For the second part of the activity give children instructions about the number of items to draw and the type of sign to use.	Ask the children to write an explanation of how the system of tribute contributed to the conquest of the Mexica and then all the Aztecs.

Plenary

Either as a class or in groups, plan a TV documentary about the Aztecs. Start with broad headings and then ask for suggestions as to locations, buildings and objects to film and people to interview. Portions of the programme can then be allocated for role-play.

Aztec religion

● These artefacts and buildings are all connected with the religion of the Aztecs.
Explain what each one shows about their beliefs.

Remains of a temple	A skull rack, the Great Temple, Mexico City

_____

_____

_____

_____

_____

A carving of one of the helpers of the god Tlaloc	A statue of the goddess Coatlicue

_____

_____

_____

_____

The Aztec calendar

The Aztecs used a 260-day sacred calendar in written records. There were 20 signs. The first day was crocodile, the second was wind, the third was house, and so on. After the last sign, flower, they went back to the beginning (to crocodile).

To count higher than 20, dots were also used. Each sign had a number of dots up to 13. After 13 dots, they went back to one dot.

By using both these cycles together, you can count up to 260.

● Continue the drawings of signs and dots to find out the Aztec way of writing numbers up to 40.

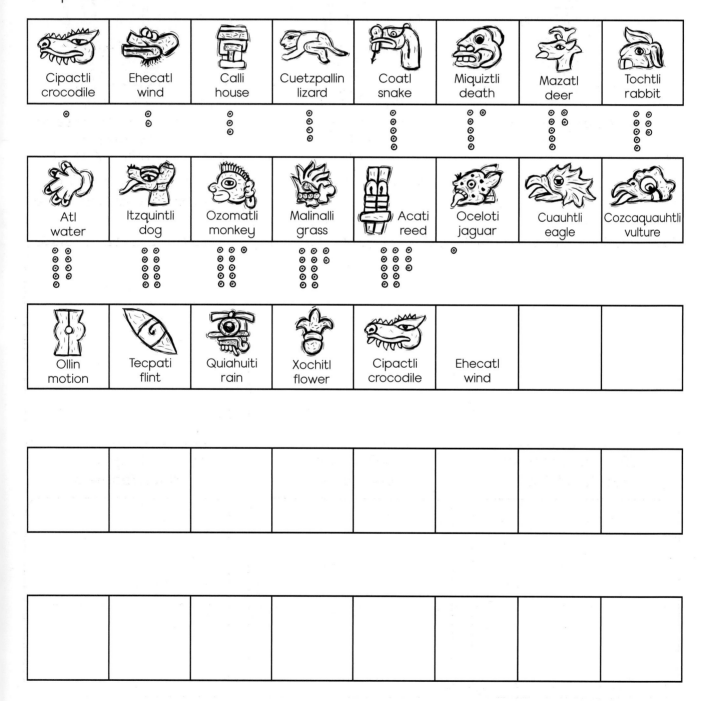

Recording tribute

For recording quantities of goods the Aztecs needed numbers higher than 20.

They used a flag for 20, a feather for 400 and an incense burner for 8000.

● Work out these examples from the *Codex Mendoza*.

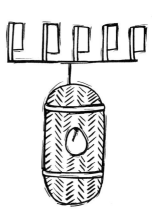

How many loads of
cocoa beans?

How many bird
pelts?

How many bundles of
feathers?

● A page from the *Codex Mendoza* lists the following items of tribute from seven towns, to be paid every six months. Draw the items and the numbers. You can draw an item more than once.

4000 mantles (cloaks)
and loincloths

800 bales of
dried chillies

20 bags of
down feathers

two war-dresses
and shields

three strings of
precious stones

two plates inlaid
with turquoise

The Ancient Greek Civilisation

Learning Objectives

Children should:
- know when and where the Ancient Greeks lived.
- understand some of the ways in which the civilisation changed over time.
- have a basic understanding of the way of life in Ancient Greece.

Background

The mountainous terrain of Greece influenced the creation of settlements that were self-sufficient and had their own identity. These city states, as they became known, shared a common language, religion and many customs. The dates given for the periods of Ancient Greek history vary; the important thing is for children to realise that the civilisation was not static and have a sense of its rise and fall. Greek society advanced and developed until about 2200BC when invaders from the north disrupted the process. The island of Crete escaped invasion and a sophisticated civilisation grew up, called Minoan after one of its kings, Minos. Gradually the mainland recovered and started to develop again. It borrowed many ideas from the Minoans, and finally became more powerful than Crete. The civilization is called Mycenaean, after its major city, Mycenae, and lasted from 1550–1000BC. The historical events that inspired legends, such as the wooden horse of Troy, took place during this period.

The way of life applies to society from the Archaic Age onwards (but not to Sparta in the Classical Age). Most houses were simple, arranged around a courtyard where work could be done in the open air. They were situated in the city, with access to temples and market, or in villages and farms around the city. Wealthy families had slaves to work for them, whereas the lives of poor families were probably not so different from those of the slaves themselves. Women could be citizens and own property but they were expected to be under the protection of a man, and education for boys and girls was completely different.

Starting Points	Main Activity	Simplified Activity	Extension Activity
C1 *'The effect of terrain and climate'* Show the area of Ancient Greece on a map of Europe. Talk generally about how terrain and climate influence settlement.	Ask the children to discuss in pairs how each aspect of life would be affected, and ask for feedback, before everyone writes.	Give children a list of statements to copy underneath the correct heading.	Ask the children to use an atlas to research more details of the terrain and climate of the area (rainfall, height of mountains) and to report to the class.
C2 *'The ages of Ancient Greece'* Explain that Ancient Greek civilisation evolved over time. Children will need access to books for their illustrations.	Read the text with the children, discussing aspects that could be illustrated. Stress that there is a range of options.	Give the children captions for each box and ask them to find and draw a suitable illustration.	Ask the children to draw a timeline of the ages and to compare the length of periods. They can also add significant events to the line.
C3 *'Way of life'* Talk about how life in Greek society would depend on wealth, sex, age and status.	Explain that some sentences generalise and that others can be used under more than one heading. Ask the children to work in pairs or groups.	Ask the children to work with a partner who will help them to read the sentences and discuss each one.	Give the children suitable resources and ask them to write one more sentence for each heading.

Plenary

Divide the board in two; write titles 'Permanent' (for climate and terrain) and 'Subject to change' (for way of life). Give the children A4 sheets. Ask them to recall what they have learned so far in sentences and place them under the correct heading. You could invite them to 'grade' changeable features: language, for instance, is more stable than the form of political organisation.

The effect of terrain and climate

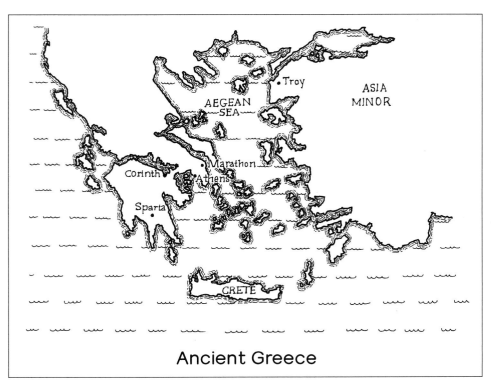

Ancient Greece

Look at this map of Ancient Greece. The people would have often travelled by sea between the islands in wooden boats.

● Write how terrain and climate would affect the people living in Ancient Greece. Use the clues in the box to help you.

> travel overland   size of settlements   size of fields   location of settlements
> clothes   design of houses   type of crops

Mountainous land

_____

_____

_____

_____

_____

_____

_____

_____

Mediterranean climate

_____

_____

_____

_____

_____

_____

_____

_____

The ages of Ancient Greece

- Illustrate this text about the different periods of Ancient Greek history. Give each illustration a caption.

The Dark Age 1000–750BC

This name is given because not much is known about this period. There was no writing, no great palaces or temples and not much trading. The size of settlements became smaller. Pottery had simple decoration – geometric designs instead of pictures. This time is sometimes called the Geometric period.

The Archaic Age 750–500BC

'Archaic' means very old, so this period is compared to the ones that came later. The communities were becoming more powerful and developing new art and architecture. The Greeks began to organise themselves in a new way, sharing power instead of having a king. The communities were called city states and were governed either by a group called an oligarchy, or by all of the male citizens (people who were not slaves). This was called a democracy. The population grew bigger and people sailed to find new farmland and metal ore. They founded colonies all around the Mediterranean.

The Classical Age 500–336BC

In this period the city state of Athens became the most powerful. It led the other Greek city states in fighting off attacks from the Persians. The Battle of Marathon was fought in this period. After the Persian Wars, the city states fought each other on the side of Athens or Sparta. This made them weak and they were taken over by King Philip of Macedon (north of Greece). This is probably the best known period in Ancient Greek history. We know a lot about how people lived at this time and our image of the Ancient Greeks is probably most influenced by classical art and literature.

The Hellenistic Age 336–31BC

King Philip's son is known as Alexander the Great. He led the Greeks in a military campaign and established a huge empire. When he died in 323BC his generals divided the empire and ruled as kings. In Greece people remembered the democracy of the past and asked for help from the Romans. The Romans 'freed' the Greeks but they were then under Roman power. When some city states rebelled they were crushed by the Romans. Greece became part of the Roman Empire.

Way of life

● Cut out the boxes and sort them into the following groups:

women   men   girls   boys   babies   slaves

They could not use their own name.	They stayed at home and learned household skills.	They could own property.
They sometimes helped in the fields.	They ran the home and brought up children.	They participated in politics.
They usually married in their twenties.	Their lives were controlled by men.	They did not go into the women's rooms in the house.
They spent most of their time at home.	They were presented to the father when they were born.	They usually married when they were teenagers.
They stayed at home, helping in the fields, fishing and sailing when they were young.	At the age of 6 or 7 they started going to school.	They spent a lot of time away from home.
They worked in fields, factories, mines, ships and other people's homes.	They kept fit for battle by playing sports.	They might be left to die or be adopted if the father did not want them.

The Battle of Marathon

Learning Objectives

Children should:
- understand how Greek training, tactics, armour and weapons helped to win the Battle of Marathon.
- appreciate the significance of the battle in Ancient Greek history.

Background

We know about the Persian Wars from Greek historians; Herodotus interviewed many survivors and their families to find out what happened. The Athenians had sought protection from the Persian Empire in the past, but had helped the Ionians to rebel against them, hence the Persians attacked Athens. According to Greek historians, the ten generals debated the attack on the Persian army from the mountains above. Five were in favour and five were against. The casting vote in favour of an immediate attack was by Callimachus, the 'war-ruler' for that year. The plain of Marathon is a crescent shape, between a semi-circle of mountains and the sea. It is six miles from end to end and two miles from shore to mountains at the widest point. The Athenian army was hidden by pine, olive and cypress trees.

Ancient Greece is known as the cradle of Western civilisation and the Battle of Marathon is seen as a key event, when the threat of the despotic East was warded off by a tiny state of free thinkers. After the battle the other Greek states supported Athens in fighting off further Persian attacks. Athens became supreme among the states and in the next two centuries Athenian culture and the notion of democracy spread across Europe. Phidippides, a professional runner, was sent 140 miles across the mountains from Marathon to Sparta to ask for help. He ran another 140 miles back with the news about the full moon (see page 41). He participated in the battle. After it, he ran 26 miles to Athens with the news of victory and a warning that the remaining Persian ships were sailing around to attack. Not surprisingly, he died of exhaustion.

Starting Points	Main Activity	Simplified Activity	Extension Activity
C4 *'The Persians land at Marathon'* Explain the reason for the Persian attack. Show on a map the relative sizes of the state of Athens and the Persian Empire. Show pictures of Greek armour and fighting formations.	Allow time for children to study the sheet and answer any questions about vocabulary. Cutting out the statements and sorting them into 'for' and 'against' will help. Seat the children in groups to discuss and vote.	Ask the children to work with a partner who will read the statements with them and encourage them to discuss each one.	Ask the children to write a formal speech, using persuasive language, in favour of either attack or delay. Ask them to practise and deliver the speech to the class.
C5 *'The battle'* Explain the geography of the plain and discuss how much space would be occupied by an army of 100 000. Make sure the terms wing, centre, and formation are understood.	Choose a symbol to represent each of the ten Athenian tribes and one for the Plataeans. Allow time for the class to read and discuss the text in pairs. Invite individuals to explain and draw on a large size copy of the diagram, before completing their own.	Provide a simplified version of the events of the battle and ask the children to draw the diagram.	Ask the children to write an imaginative account of the battle from the point of view of a surviving Persian soldier.
C6 *'The consequences of the battle'* Discuss the results of the battle and the reasons why it is seen as so important. Tell the story of Phidippides.	Ask the children to recall and write the consequences in their own words and to write the story on a separate sheet.	Give the children a few 'closed' questions about the consequences. *Did the Persians conquer Europe? Did Athens become stronger?* Ask them to write the Phidippides story.	Give the children suitable resources. Ask them to read about the night march of Miltiades to Athens to ward off a possible further attack, and to report to the class.

Plenary

Give out sentences describing the sequence of events to members of the class. Ask individuals to peg their sentences on a line in the correct sequence. Ask the children to recall further details.

The Persians land at Marathon

In 490BC Persian troops landed at Marathon, on the shore of the state of Athens (Attica). The Athenian army assembled on the hills above, lead by ten generals. Imagine you are one of these generals. You have to decide whether to attack the Persians straightaway, or whether to wait for the Spartan army. The Spartans will not leave before full moon, for religious reasons, and the moon is now in its sixth day. Cut out the boxes and sort them into 'for' and 'against' the battle. Discuss in a group and take a vote.

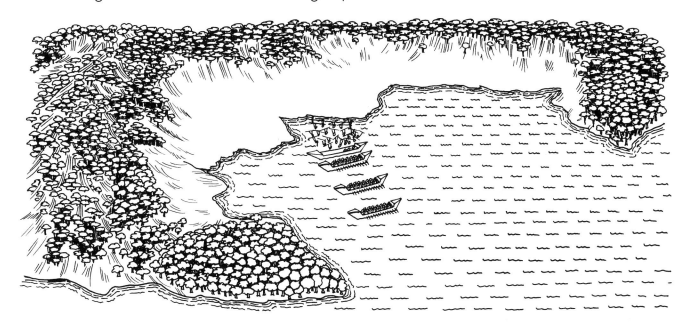

The soldiers of your army have long spears, short swords, helmets, breastplates, shields and greaves (leg protection).

Your soldiers are very well trained. They know how to keep formation.

The Persian soldiers are not so well trained.

The Persian army is made of a mixture of troops from different parts of the Persian Empire. It includes cavalry, archers and infantry with no body armour or wicker shields, and poorer weapons than your soldiers.

The Persian army has a strong reputation; they have always beaten the Greeks in the past.

There are about 10 000 Greeks and at the last minute an army of 1000 from the state of Plataea joins you.

There are about 100 000 Persians.

The Spartans have undoubtedly the strongest army in Greece.

The Persian army cannot see you, as you are hidden in the trees. They would see you when you got down to the plain.

You can see the whole Persian army on the plain below you.

The Persians have a very experienced general called Datis.

Your soldiers are keen to defend their freedom.

The battle

- The 11 generals decided to attack immediately – by one vote! Miltiades was voted commander. Usually, the Greeks advanced in a block, called a phalanx, eight men deep. Miltiades had a different plan. Read this description of the battle and complete the diagram to show the location of the Greeks and their tactics.

The Persians were camped on a wide area of plain below. If the Greeks attacked the middle of the Persian army, the other Persians could come round the side. The cavalry would be able to chase them from behind.

Miltiades instructed the other generals to spread out the soldiers to cover the widest area possible. The thinnest line would be the centre, where it was easier for the men to close in; the two wings were thicker. There were ten Athenian tribes. The Plataeans were on the extreme left.

They descended under the cover of the trees. They had to cover flat unoccupied ground to reach the Persian army. At this point they could be seen. Normally they would advance at a slow pace but Miltiades commanded them to run so that the Persians would not have time to get organised.

Only the Persian infantry had time to form. They fought back but were killed in large numbers by the Greeks. Eventually, with their greater numbers, the Persians broke through the centre of the Greek line and this section retreated back into a valley and up on to higher ground to re-group. Miltiades than commanded the two wings, which had kept formation, to close in on the centre of the Persian army.

By evening the Persians retreated back to their ships and the Greeks chased them. The heaviest losses on the Greek side were from trying to set fire to the Persian ships.

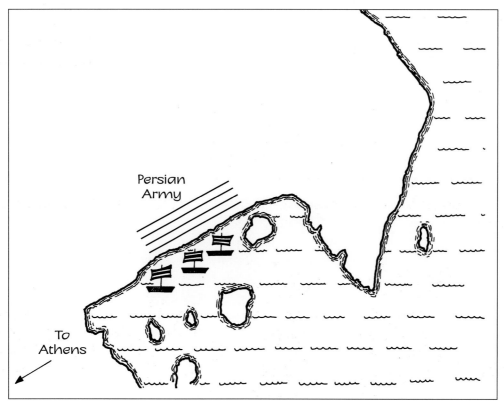

Persian Army

To Athens

The consequences of the battle

- Explain the things that happened as a consequence of the battle.

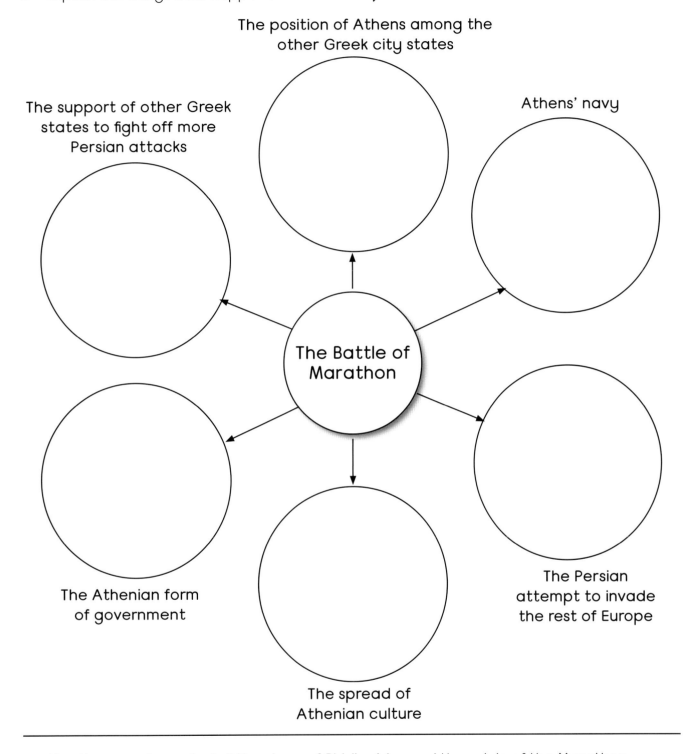

The position of Athens among the other Greek city states

The support of other Greek states to fight off more Persian attacks

Athens' navy

The Battle of Marathon

The Athenian form of government

The spread of Athenian culture

The Persian attempt to invade the rest of Europe

- Use these cartoons to tell the story of Phidippides and the origin of the Marathon running race.

Athens and Sparta

Learning Objectives

Children should:
- know the main differences in laws, customs and education between Athens and Sparta.
- understand some of the reasons for these differences.

Background

The state of Sparta was founded in the tenth century BC, and between 740–720BC the Spartans invaded the neighbouring state of Messenia. At the beginning of the Archaic period they were trading with other states, importing luxury goods, producing fine metalware and vases. They also developed music and poetry. However, when they lost a war and the Messenians began a revolt, in order to defend themselves, the Spartans adopted an overwhelmingly militaristic culture at the expense of all else. Hence they were the strongest military power at the beginning of the Classical period.

The Persian army invaded the state of Athens at Marathon in 490BC (see previous section). To prepare for a second invasion, Athens built up its navy to be the most powerful in Greece and defeated the Persians at sea; an army led by the Spartan general defeated them on land (479BC). To be ready for any more attacks the 'Delian league' of city states was formed under the leadership of Athens. The period 479–431BC is known as the Golden Age of Athens. It became very wealthy and a centre for democracy, the arts and philosophy.

After the Persian Wars, the two strongest states became rivals, each with their allies. The wars between them (Peloponnesian, after the Spartan peninsula) destroyed Athens, weakened the whole of Greece and made it vulnerable to invasion.

Starting Points	Main Activity	Simplified Activity	Extension Activity
C7 *'Athens'*, **C8** *'Sparta'* and **C9** *'Comparing Athens and Sparta'* **Lesson 1** Explain that the city states rivalled each other but would ally against an outside invader. Explain briefly the reasons for Sparta's change in culture.	Explain that pupils will become experts on either Athens or Sparta. Give them one of the two pages. Allow them to work in pairs to fill in the table for the same city. Stress that they will need to be very familiar with the information for the next lesson.	Give the children a list of statements about one of the cities. Make sure that they understand the statements and ask them to write them in the correct box on the table. Ask them to draw a picture or diagram that will help them to remember each fact.	The activity can be extended by providing additional resources for research, giving children more of an opportunity to be an expert on their city state.
Lesson 2 Explain how the two states came to be powerful and also rivals.	Seat the children in pairs, ready to exchange information. Emphasise that this should be done verbally, not by swapping sheets and reading, or copying. If necessary allocate a time for verbal exchange before any writing is allowed.	Seat the children in pairs of similar ability and encourage them to give information in their own words, using their drawings as reminders.	Give the children resources about the wars between Athens and Sparta. Ask them to research the main events and report to the class.
Lesson 3 Recap on the differences between the states.	Ask the children to design a poster for Athens or Sparta, as if to attract tourists. Explain this as a fun way of showing the differences between the cities, and that mass tourism is a modern phenomena! Discuss the way posters give a place an image, the sorts of pictures that would portray Athens and Sparta, and the sort of person the poster might seek to attract.		

Plenary

Recap on the main points by asking children to show their posters, and discussing the aspects of life they have chosen to portray. Stage a role-play where children play Athenians or Spartans and defend their lifestyle.

Athens

● Read about Athens and fill in the column headed 'Athens' on worksheet C9.

During the wars against Persia, Athens built up a powerful navy. It became the leader of a league of city states. The soil around their city was poor and the population was big. They gave protection to other cities in return for food. Their own preferred form of government was democracy, where all the male citizens had a chance to participate in making laws.

Athens was well known for poetry, drama, art, beautiful buildings and great thinkers. Its citizens believed it was important to develop both the body and the mind. They wanted a society of good citizens and strong soldiers. They also enjoyed the comforts of life, good food and wine. They were proud of their city and its achievements. Athenians believed that human life was controlled by the gods. They prayed and made sacrifices to the gods.

Most people lived in a family group – parents and children. Women spent most of their time at home, sometimes going out to visit friends or attend festivals. Girls were educated at home. Their parents arranged for them to get married in their teens.

Boys lived at home and went to primary school where the most important subjects were the works of Homer, a famous Greek poet, and how to play the lyre, a stringed instrument. In high school they would learn other subjects, like Maths and Science. They had to do lots of gymnastics and sport to keep fit. Men did physical exercise every day so that they would be fit for battle. They could also spend time on politics, cultural activities and entertaining friends.

Sparta

- Read about Sparta and fill in the column headed 'Sparta' on worksheet C9.

In 500BC Sparta had become the most powerful of the city states because of their army. Spartans were proud of their city and very loyal. Other cities accepted the protection of Sparta's army. This was useful to Sparta because their soil was not good enough to grow grain and they had a large army to feed. Sparta was governed by an oligarchy, a group of men who made laws for everybody else.

The aim of Spartan society was to keep the army strong. No great poets, artists or architects came from Sparta. It was important to have a perfect body; babies with any defects were taken away by soldiers and left to die or brought up to be slaves. People believed in discipline and a simple life with no luxuries. As for all Greeks, religion was part of their lives. They believed in gods who might favour them or be angry with them. They tried to please the gods with sacrifices.

Boys' education began at age 6 or 7. Reading and writing were not very important; they learned survival skills and military training. They lived away from home at the barracks (soldiers' accommodation).

Girls went away to live in a barracks at the age of 6 or 7, like the boys. They did gymnastics, wrestling and combat skills. This was so that they would have strong babies. At 18, if she passed a fitness test, a girl was assigned a husband and allowed to go home. Boys stayed on in the army, if they passed the test. They could marry but not live with their wives and children until they were 30 years old, and not leave the army until age 60. Women had quite a lot of freedom because the men were all away from home.

Comparing Athens and Sparta

Lesson 1: Read about either Athens or Sparta and make notes in the table.
Lesson 2: Discuss what you have found out with a partner. Complete the empty column of the table. Decide how similar or different the two cities were for each heading.

	Athens	Sparta	Similar or different?
Aim of society			
Type of government			
Education of boys			
Education of girls			
Home life			
Art and culture			
Relations with other cities			
Religion			

Ancient Greek Gods and Theatre

Learning Objectives

Children should:
- know the names and characteristics of the principal Ancient Greek gods.
- know how Ancient Greek theatre evolved and the ways in which it led to, but also differed from, theatre today.

Background

The Greeks believed in many gods, the controllers of human life and death. These gods were subject to human feelings such as anger, love and jealousy. They interacted with humans, often appearing in another form. They could have offspring with humans. They intervened in the lives of humans, helping their favourites. Greeks, therefore, offered sacrifices and appealed to the gods to act in their favour. There was a hierarchy among the gods and the 12 most important (described on page 49) lived on Mount Olympus. Phenomena of the natural world were explained in stories or ideas about the gods. Poseidon caused earthquakes; plague and death came from the arrows of Artemis.

Evolving from religious rites dating back to at least 1200BC, the Greek drama evolved into a form that has lasted to the present day. Plays by Sophocles and Euripides, for example, are still among the greatest works of theatre. Note that for the sequence on page 50, the building of theatres is simultaneous with the changes introduced in form; allow it to be placed 3rd, 4th or 5th.

Starting Points	Main Activity	Simplified Activity	Extension Activity
C10 *'The gods'* Make available resources about the gods and allow time for study either as a class or in groups. Also have ready examples of figures portrayed on Greek vases.	Use the activity to consolidate the children's knowledge and to combine this with a study of the style of Greek vases. Discuss some examples of the way in which gods could be portrayed.	Give the children a copy of the sheet on which the matching task has been partially filled in and ask them to complete it.	Ask the children to research the relationships between the gods and to draw a diagram to represent this.
C11 *'History of Ancient Greek theatre'* Explain that the origins of theatre today come from Ancient Greece.	Introduce the activity as a puzzle. Remind children that grammar and content can give clues to sequence. Ask them to do the task in pairs and check as a class.	Simplify the text to headings (a religious festival in the country, a competition every year, a story told by a group of 12 and one actor). Ask the children to order the headings.	Provide suitable resources; ask the children to research the three writers mentioned in the text and to report to the class.
C12 *'Design for a play'* Have ready a suitable myth or legend to read as the plot or a play. Alternatively, ask children to research and have one prepared.	Ask the children to read the information and discuss the differences between an Ancient Greek and a modern play. Remind the children that each character can have several masks.	Give the children a plot and list of characters and ask them to design masks and costume for a specific number of characters.	Ask the children to go on to write a scene from the play: an introduction by the chorus and some dialogue between characters.

Plenary

Ask the children to recall what they have learned about the theatre and to describe what it would be like to be in the audience. Recall the names and characteristics of the gods by asking how each one might be recognised as a character in a play.

The gods

● Match the names of these gods to the description.

> Ares   Apollo   Artemis   Hera   Demeter   Dionysus
>
> Hermes   Zeus   Athena   Poseidon   Pluto   Aphrodite

Goddess of all plants. Her symbol is a sheaf of wheat or barley. _____	The ruler of the gods and commander of the heavens. His symbols were the thunderbolt, the eagle and the oak tree. _____	Wife of Zeus and the goddess of marriage. Her symbols were the pomegranate and the peacock. _____
The goddess of love and beauty. She was born in the sea and rode to shore in a scallop shell. Her symbols were roses, doves, sparrows, dolphins and rams. _____	The god of sun, light and truth. His symbol was the laurel tree. He killed his mother's enemy, the serpent python. _____	The goddess of wisdom and war. She is portrayed with armour. Her symbols were the owl and the olive tree. _____
The god of wine and fertility. He taught people how to make wine. He carried a special staff. _____	The ruler of the underworld and guardian of the dead. He drove a gold chariot with black horses. _____	The moon goddess. She is portrayed with a bow and arrow. Her symbols were the cypress tree, deer and dogs. _____
The brother of Zeus and the ruler of the seas. He lived in an underwater palace and kept a gold chariot and white horses. He carried a trident (a three-pointed spear). _____	The messenger of the gods. He wore a winged helmet and sandals and carried a staff. _____	The god of war. His symbols were a burning torch, spear, dogs and vultures. _____

● Choose one of the gods and design an illustration in the style of a Greek vase.

History of Ancient Greek theatre

- Sequence these developments to give a history of the theatre in Ancient Greece.

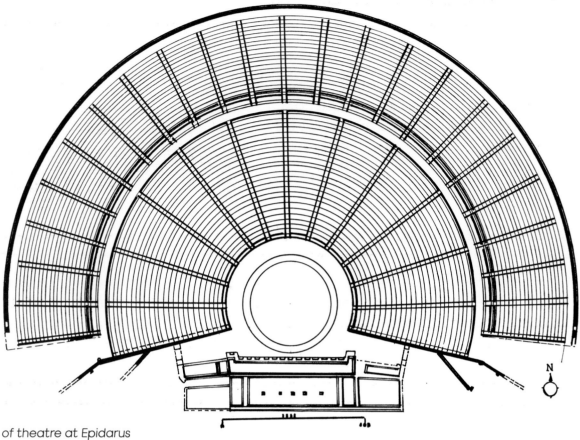

Plan of theatre at Epidarus

Open air theatres were built. A semi-circle of stone seats surrounded a round stage.

Sophocles introduced a third actor. His plays focused more on the human characters and less on the gods. Eventually, actors became the most important part of the drama; more so than the chorus that only commented on events.

Greeks in the countryside in some city states held festivals to celebrate the god, Dionysus. The festivals became more popular until they were an annual event throughout Greece.

In Athens the festival became a more formal competition. Songs were composed and dances performed by a group of up to 50 men. There were prizes for the best. The performances were in the market place.

Later, a writer called Aeschylus added a second actor (the antagonist), props, and scenery. He reduced the chorus from 50 to 12. He is known as the first playwright.

In about 530BC, a writer called Thespis introduced a protagonist – an actor who exchanged dialogue with the leader of the chorus.

Design for a play

- Use this information to design background, costumes and props for a play. Choose a Greek myth or legend as the plot of your play.

Masks

The actors were all male. They used masks to play a number of parts and to indicate how the character was feeling. The masks also helped to amplify their voices so they would be heard by everyone. Female masks had bigger mouths and eyes.

Costume

The theatres were very big and to make themselves more visible to the audience, the actors would wear costumes with padded clothing, large wigs, and thick-soled shoes. The happy characters wore bright colours and the tragic characters wore dark colours.

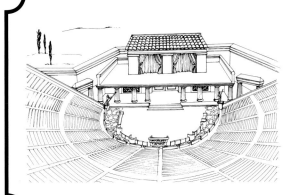

Set

The actors appeared on a raised stage and the chorus was in the circular area below. The back wall of the raised stage was often painted to look like the setting for the play. There were two doors at the back of the stage that could be opened, a platform was wheeled out to show the body of a character who had been killed. (Characters were not killed on stage. The chorus would tell the audience what had happened.)

Summary of myth or legend:

_____

_____

_____

_____

_____

List of characters:

_____

_____

_____

_____

_____

- Use a separate sheet to draw masks, costumes and a scene.

Comparing Ancient Greece with Today

Learning Objectives

Children should:
- be able to compare aspects of Ancient Greek culture with modern British culture.
- appreciate how aspects of modern Western European culture have their origins in Ancient Greece.

Background

The original Olympics were held every four years in July or August. In the beginning, the Games lasted only one day and comprised of only one event, but gradually more events were added and towards the fifth century BC, the games lasted for five days. All male Greeks who were free citizens and had not committed murder or heresy, had the right to take part. Women were strictly prohibited from even watching. The athletes presented themselves at Elis, the organising town, one month before the Games began. Two days before the beginning of the Games, a procession of athletes and judges started to arrive in Olympia, which was full of the crowds who had come to watch. The ceremonies began with the official oath taken by the athletes at the altar of Zeus, swearing that they would compete with honour and respect the rules.

The Greek alphabet was adapted from Phoenician characters. It was adopted by the Etruscans (Northern Italy). From there it evolved to become the Roman/Latin alphabet. In the Latin alphabet the letter 'G' was designed to replace the Greek letter 'Z' (not needed in Latin). The letter 'R' evolved as a variation of 'P'. The Latin alphabet contained 21 letters; it excluded J, U, W, Y and Z. The Greek letters 'Y' and 'Z' were added during the first century BC, following the Roman conquest of Greece (in order to accommodate the 'borrowed' Greek word sounds). 'J', 'U' and 'W' were added during the Middle Ages.

Starting Points	Main Activity	Simplified Activity	Extension Activity
G1 *'The Olympic Games'* Talk about the Olympic Games today, covering the headings on page 53.	Ask the children to complete the table in pairs. Use the information as a basis for discussion of the original Olympics.	Give the children a copy of the sheet with the headings filled in and a list of sentences about today's Olympics to copy into the correct box.	Ask the children to write further research questions for the Olympics and provide suitable resources for the task.
G2 *'Greek schools'* Recall what children remember about education from previous work on Ancient Greece.	Ask the children to read the text and to underline key words that highlight differences from school now. Discuss as a class before asking them to write a summary.	Give the children a copy of the sheet with specific questions to answer. Ask them to work with a partner who will help them to read the text.	Ask the children to use the information in the text to write a description of the vase painting, as for a museum display.
G3 *'The Greek alphabet'* Explain how our alphabet can be traced back to the Ancient Greeks and that it has some characters that have to be represented by two letters in English; there is not a letter for letter equivalent.	Allow time for children to study and talk about the alphabet and begin noting some of the differences. There are many ways these could be expressed.	Give the children a copy of the sheet with specific questions about the alphabet. Ask the children: *Which English letters are missing? How many letters are there altogether? Are any of the English letters in the same order?*	For fun, ask the children to spell some words to each other using the Greek alphabet.

Plenary

Conclude the comparison of Ancient Greece with modern Britain by listing with the children things that they would have in common with the Ancient Greeks.

The Olympic Games

- Write these headings in the table below. Complete the third column about the Olympic Games today.

Events   Purpose   Clothes   Duration and frequency
Participants   Publicity   Buildings   Venue
The effect of war on the games

	Original Olympic Games	The Games today
Purpose	To keep men fit for war, as part of a festival in honour of Zeus.	
	Five days, every four years.	
	Messengers travelled the country to announce the Games and invite teams to attend.	
	Specially built facilities for participants and spectators.	
	Olympia	
	Running, wrestling, boxing, chariot race, horse race.	
	Participants wore no clothes.	
	Male-only teams from each of the city states.	
	The war stopped while the games were being held.	

Greek schools

- Read about school in Ancient Greece and list the ways in which it was different from school today.

Most children didn't go to school: many of them were slaves; others were from poor families and had to work at home; all girls stayed at home. So it was only boys from families who could afford to pay the teacher who went; they attended from the age of about 7–13. A slave might go with them to make sure they paid attention.

The schools were small – perhaps up to 20 boys. The first teacher was called a 'grammatistes'. He taught reading, writing and arithmetic. The pupils wrote with a stylus on a wooden tablet covered with wax. In the second school the teacher was a 'kitharistes' who taught boys to play the lyre and pipes and to recite poetry off by heart. In the third school the 'paidotribes' taught dancing and athletics. They could go to a 'gymnasium' to practise.

When they had finished school, young men could continue their education by going to special teachers called 'sophists' and learning the art of public speaking. They could gather round a philosopher and discuss politics, history, science and mathematics. In the later years (Hellenistic period) there were often libraries and lecture rooms at the gymnasia.

Differences:

_____

_____

_____

_____

_____

_____

_____

_____

The Greek alphabet

The alphabet used by the Greeks of the Classical Age is shown here. It was used for Latin, changing over time, and the Latin alphabet was used to write English. Compare it to the English alphabet and describe the differences you find.

capital letter	lower case	sound	name of letter
A	α	a	alpha
B	β	b	beta
Γ	γ	g	gamma
Δ	δ	d	delta
E	ε	e	epsilon
Z	ς	z	zeta
H	η	ay or e	eta
Θ	θ	th	theta
I	ι	i	iota
K	κ	k	kappa
Λ	λ	l	lambda
M	μ	m	mu
N	ν	n	nu
Ξ	ξ	x or ks	xi
O	o	o	omicron
Π	π	p	pi
P	ρ	r	rho
Σ	σς	s	sigma
T	τ	t	tau
Y	υ	oo or u	upsilon
Φ	φ	ph or f	phi
X	χ	ch	chi
Ψ	ψ	ps	psi
Ω	ω	oh	omega

Differences:

_____

_____

_____

_____

_____

Myths, Language and Learning

Learning Objectives

Children should:
- understand that Ancient Greece has contributed to our learning and language.
- appreciate the ways in which Greek mythology has inspired artists of a later age.

Background

One of the functions of a myth is to explain natural phenomena. Persephone was the beautiful daughter of Demeter, goddess of fertility. Hades, guardian of the underworld, fell in love with her and took her down to his realm. Demeter stopped the plants from growing, until Persephone was allowed to return to her for part of the year. Spring is when Persephone returns to her mother, delivered by the god Hermes, and autumn is when she has to go back to the underworld.

The Greeks were among the earliest societies to search for a new way of understanding the world. Their thinkers covered many different areas of human knowledge and established lines of enquiry that continue to the present day.

Nothing certain is known about the Greek poet Homer, credited as the author of the two great works, *The Iliad* and *The Odyssey*. He lived around 850BC, possibly as much as 100 years later. *The Iliad* tells the story of the Greek war against Troy (in present-day Turkey). Though the stories are mythical, there is evidence that such a war took place. *The Odyssey* tells the amazing adventures of Odysseus, trying to return to his home in Ithaca after the war, and must be fictional.

Starting Points	Main Activity	Simplified Activity	Extension Activity
G4 *'Words from Ancient Greek'* Recall literacy work on suffixes and prefixes. Explain that knowing the origin of an affix in another language can help us to understand the word.	Allow the children to work through the task in pairs and to share examples. You could divide the class into teams and award points for each example they think of – one per affix.	Provide dictionaries and ask the children to find words with Greek prefixes. If you have teams, make sure there is one child with a dictionary per team.	Give the children a list of challenging vocabulary with Greek affixes and ask them to deduce the meaning (e.g. pseudonym, bibliophile, theology).
G5 *'Greek mythology'* Talk about myths and legends, recalling those the children know. Tell or read the story of Persephone. Briefly introduce *The Iliad* and *The Odyssey*.	Discuss the painting as a class before asking children to write about the scene depicted. Talk about ways that the artist has exploited the drama of the scene and encourage them to use similar techniques in a sketch for a painting.	Give the children a copy of the sheet with specific questions about the painting and ask them to write answers. Ask them to work with a partner who will help them to read the story adapted from *The Odyssey*.	Talk with the children about their sketches and ways that they could be improved. Provide, brushes, paper and paint for them to produce the painting.
G6 *'Great Greek thinkers'* Talk about the development from explaining the world by myth to using scientific or logical enquiry.	Ask the children to read about the discoveries in pairs and to agree on the missing words. Discuss each discovery as a class.	Give the children a copy of the sheet with just two or three of the discoveries and missing words to complete.	Provide the children with measuring cylinders, balls of plasticine and water. Ask them to use Archimedes' theory to find out the volume of the ball.

Plenary

Hold a quiz on Ancient Greek myths and thinkers. Seat the children in groups and ask them to write questions on cards. Either limit the quiz to what children have studied as a class or provide resources for them to research further questions and answers.

Words from Ancient Greek

● Many words, or parts of words, in modern English come from Ancient Greek. Look at the Greek affixes and their meanings.

anti	against	micro	small
astro	star	mis	hate, wrong
auto	self	mono	one
biblio	book	onym	name
bio	life	phil	love
chron	time	phob	fear
cosmo	world	phon	sound
cracy	government	poly	many
dem	people	pseudo	false
geo	earth	psych	mind
graph	write	scop	see
hydro	water	soph	wisdom
hyper	over (too much)	syn	together
log	speech, word	tele	at a distance
logy	science, study	theo	God or god
meter	measure	therm	heat

● Give the meaning of these words:

Demo-cracy _____

Thermo-meter _____

Auto-bio-graphy _____

● Find more examples of words with one or two Greek affixes.

● Write the word for:

sound at a distance _____

study of the mind _____

fear of water _____

Greek mythology

The stories of Greek mythology have inspired artists through the ages. Find out about the story of Persephone and explain the scene that Frederic Leighton has re-created in his painting *The Return of Persephone* (1890–91).

_____

_____

_____

_____

_____

_____

_____

_____

_____

_____

_____

- Read this story adapted from *The Odyssey* by the poet Homer, which tells the adventures of Odysseus on his way back to Greece after the Trojan wars. Sketch a picture to illustrate it.

The sirens were bird-like creatures with female human heads. They lived on an island and lured sailors to their death with beautiful singing and music. The clever Odysseus blocked up his sailors' ears with wax so that they couldn't hear the music. He wanted to hear it himself so he told his sailors to tie him to the mast, and not to let him go, however much he begged them. The plan worked and the ship sailed past the sirens.

Great Greek thinkers

● Read about the discoveries and fill in the missing words.

> eclipse   water   radius   triangle   interviewed
>
> rules   sun   travelled

Archimedes realised that you could find out the exact volume of an object by measuring the amount of _____ it displaces. It is said that he thought of this idea when he was in the bath!

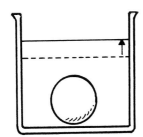

Anaxagoras realised that the moon does not shine with its own light; it reflects light from the _____ . He worked out that a solar _____ was caused by the moon passing in front of the sun.

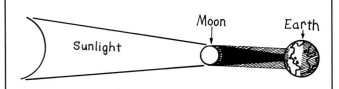

Pythagoras worked out that to find the circumference of a circle, you have to measure the _____ and multiply it by a number he called π (pi) – 3.142, then multiply by 2.

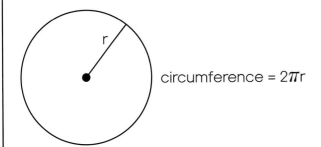

circumference = $2\pi r$

Pythagoras also worked out that in a right-angled _____ , the square of the long side (hypotenuse) is the same as the sum of the squares of the other two sides.

$b^2 + c^2 = a^2$

Herodotus is known as the first true historian. After the Persian Wars he _____ many survivors and their families to find out what happened, and wrote a history of the wars. He also _____ and wrote about other people.

Plato studied the best way for people to rule a state. He created _____ for good government.

Buildings and Collections

Learning Objectives

Children should:
- appreciate the influence that Ancient Greek architecture has had on later periods.
- consider the advantages and possible controversy regarding museum collections of Ancient Greek artefacts.

Background

Doric, the most simple style of Ancient Greek architecture, worked well on long rectangular buildings. The Parthenon is the most famous example. Ionic columns were taller, giving a more slender impression, and the style is more decorative. Corinthian, popular with the Romans, was the most decorative. Roofs were flat. The buildings of Ancient Greece were used as models for architecture in Britain from the 1700s. The resulting style is known as 'neoclassical'.

Artefacts from Ancient Greece can be seen in museums across Europe and in the USA. This means that they can be preserved by specialists in conservation and viewed by a wide audience, including students and artists. The Parthenon sculptures were acquired by Lord Elgin between 1801–10. In 1816 they were acquired by the British Museum. Calls for their return to Greece began as early as 1833 but on the re-establishment of democracy in Greece in 1974 it became a cause of the new government and the subject of much publicity. British governments have always stated that the sculptures are the legal property of the museum and any decision should be taken by its trustees.

Starting Points	Main Activity	Simplified Activity	Extension Activity
G7 *'Ancient Greek buildings'* Show sketches of architectural styles and introduce vocabulary that will help the children to describe the pictures.	Ask the children to discuss the buildings in pairs and to look for 1) features that all of them have in common 2) distinguishing features. This will help to structure their writing.	Give the children pictures of two buildings and ask them to write a sentence to describe each common feature.	Provide suitable resources and ask the children to research the uses of these or similar buildings. Ask them to explain how the design matches the use of the building.
G8 *'Ancient Greek influence on architecture in Britain'* Prepare a photograph of, or a walk, to sketch a building in neoclassical style in your area.	Tell the children how you want them to mark the pictures to show the Greek influence. Either use a photo or take the children to see a neoclassical building for their sketch.	Seat the children in pairs of similar ability and encourage them to give information in their own words, using their drawings as reminders.	Ask the children to sketch a design for a new building in neoclassical style.
G9 *'Museum collections'* Discuss the way museums acquire collections and how they combine conservation with making them available to the public.	Allow time for the children to read the texts and look at the pictures. Ask them to think of reasons in pairs and then pool ideas as a class. Follow the same procedure for the third text and picture.	Give the children a copy of the sheet with specific questions to answer. *Which people would find a museum collection useful? What would happen to artefacts that were not cared for?*	Ask the children to contact (letter, phone or email) a local museum and find out about cleaning and conservation methods. Ask them to report to the class.

Plenary

Ask the children to plan a TV documentary on 'The Greek Legacy'. Ask them to compile a list of topics to cover and suggest a running order of locations for filming.

Ancient Greek buildings

- Use these pictures of Ancient Greek buildings to write a description of 'classical' architecture.

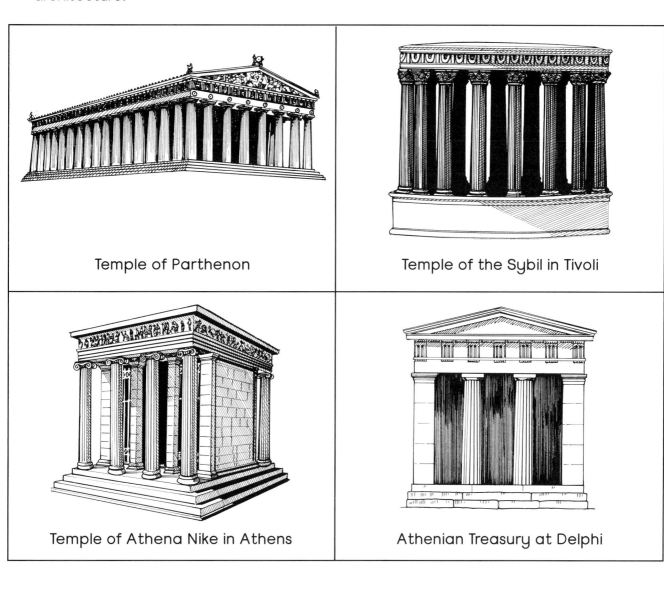

Temple of Parthenon	Temple of the Sybil in Tivoli
Temple of Athena Nike in Athens	Athenian Treasury at Delphi

_____

_____

_____

_____

_____

_____

_____

_____

Ancient Greek influence on architecture in Britain

- Draw arrows or shade to show where you see 'classical' influence in these buildings.

Blenheim Palace

The British Museum

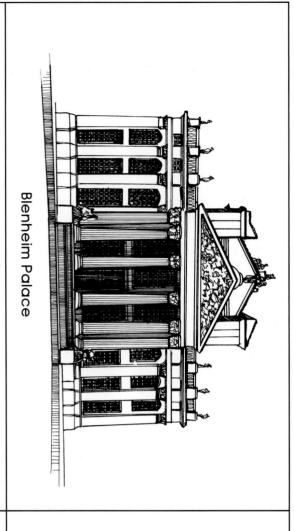
Edinburgh University

- Find a building in your area with classical influence and draw it.

FOLENS HISTORY IN ACTION 6

Museum collections

The artefacts illustrated on this page are in the collection of the British Museum in London.

This bronze head from a huge statue of Aphrodite was found in north-east Turkey by a man digging his field in 1872. It was sold to the museum by an Italian dealer. A bronze hand was found nearby, but the rest of the body has never been found.

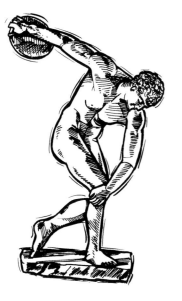

This marble statue was copied from a bronze statue of the fifth century BC. The head has been wrongly restored; it should be facing back to look at the discus. The discus was part of the pentathlon and these athletes were admired for their physical appearance because the different events meant that their bodies stayed in proportion.

● List the reasons why museum collections are valuable to us now.

_____

_____

_____

This frieze is from a collection given to the museum by Lord Elgin. The 'Elgin Marbles' are carvings that decorated the Parthenon, the temple in Athens.

The Greek government wants the British Museum to return the marbles to Greece.
● What do you think the museum should do?

_____

_____

_____

John Lennon

Learning Objectives

Children should:
- know key biographical details about John Lennon.
- know relevant information about the era he grew up in.

Background

Lennon was from a working-class background and went to the local grammar school. He was clearly intelligent and of a questioning nature, and consequently something of a rebel. His aunt got him a place at art college but he was more interested in music.

For the first time, teenagers in the Fifties stopped dressing like their parents, had their own money to spend, and their own music. Music might be heard on the radio, but a lot of music from the USA was not played so teenagers went to cafés where they could listen to a jukebox. If they had money, they could buy singles (45 rpm) or LPs (long playing records at 33 rpm), played on a gramophone. 'Teddy boys' were one of the first teenage cults; John and the other Beatles originally fell into the 'Rockers' category of 'Mods and Rockers'.

In the late Fifties in the USA 'trad' jazz was waning and being replaced by skiffle – blues and work songs performed on a guitar, base and drum. Some jazz musicians, like Lonnie Donegan in Britain, looked to the original roots of rock 'n' roll and created an urbanised form of blues. Between sets, Donegan played onstage using a washboard, a tea-chest bass and a cheap Spanish guitar. Lennon's first band, The Quarrymen (after his school, Quarry Bank High), was a skiffle band. Elvis Presley, Buddy Holly and Roy Orbison were also early musical influences on Lennon.

Starting Points	Main Activity	Simplified Activity	Extension Activity
L1 *'John Lennon's life'* Discuss what the children already know about Lennon and the Beatles. Show some photographs.	Ask the children to read the text and underline the events they think are most significant. Give an allotted number if necessary. Allow time for them to compare. Ask them to record the events in their own words.	Ask the children to work with a partner who will read the text with them and help them to discuss the key events.	Ask the children to write five comprehension questions based on the text and give them to a partner to answer.
L2 *'Childhood memories of John Lennon'* Show the location of Woolton and Liverpool on a map. Discuss what the children already know about the Forties and Fifties.	Explain that children should infer the information, rather than expect to find it. Give an example (text 1 implies that he was popular).	Give the children some direct questions about the text, requiring little or no inference.	Ask the children to carry out some research into music in the Fifties in preparation for the next lesson.
L3 *'Music in the Fifties'* Talk about changes in music technology and how people listened to music in the Fifties. Explain the influences on the young Lennon.	Ask the children to record what they have learned in their own words, using the pictures and captions as clues.	Give the children a list of phrases or sentences that they can match to each picture.	Ask the children to do further research on the music of the Fifties and add information to what they have already recorded.

Plenary

Put on the board the headings: 'Biographical facts', 'Personality', 'Influences in early life' and 'Music'. Ask the children to recall what they have learned and allocate it to the right category.

John Lennon's life

● Read this biography and list the events in Lennon's life that you think would be the most significant to him.

John Lennon was born at the beginning of the Second World War in Liverpool. At the age of five his father left the family and his mother, Julia, felt she could not care for him on her own. He went to live with his Aunt Mimi at 251, Menlove Avenue in Woolton, a suburb of Liverpool, but he continued to see his mother. She was killed in an accident when he was 16.

He took an early interest in music; his mother taught him to play the banjo. He wrote songs and played the guitar in the front porch of his aunt's home. When he was still a student he formed his own band. The band began to do live performances. At one of these he was introduced to Paul McCartney and invited him to join the group: The Quarrymen.

John with his Aunt Mimi

The group started playing small gigs. Paul's friend George Harrison joined in 1958 and played guitar. In 1960 John hired a manager and his best friend Stuart Sutcliffe joined to play base guitar. They changed the name several times; as 'The Silver Beetles' they did a tour of Scotland and as 'The Beatles', a few months in Germany. Stuart quit the band to concentrate on his art studies. In 1961 they began to play at The Cavern Club in Liverpool. Also in this year, John married his girlfriend, Cynthia Powell.

John and Yoko Ono

At the Cavern Club a local record store owner heard them and offered to become their manager. He got them a producer and a recording contract. They also took on a new drummer – Ringo Starr. John heard that his friend Stu had died of a brain haemorrhage and was devastated by the news. The Beatles released their first single in October 1962. Their second single, written by John, became number one and from then on they had hit after hit. The Beatles became the most successful band in the history of pop music.

John had a son called Julian with his first wife, Cynthia. He met his second wife, Yoko Ono, in the late Sixties and with her he started to go in a different direction from the Beatles. They made experimental music and attracted a lot of publicity. Staying in bed to campaign for peace was a famous example.

In 1980 Lennon had just started to make music again after a five-year break to look after their son, Sean. Coming back from the studios one night, with Yoko, he was shot several times in the back by a man with a shotgun. He died in hospital.

Most significant events:

_____

_____

_____

_____

_____

Childhood memories of John Lennon

● Like John Lennon, David Ashton grew up in Woolton, Liverpool, in the 1940s and 1950s. What do these extracts from David's memories tell us about John, and about growing up in these decades?

> John became interesting for, I guess what I would now call, his 'Huckleberry Finn' qualities. He knew things or found them out and if he liked you he got you into trouble! … John was alluring and beguiling … never boring. There were lots of kids banned from playing with the gang of Peter Shotton, Ivan Vaughan and John Lennon but we played anyway.

John as a boy

> Going to get a haircut, Bioletti, the barber, had a rule that boys always had to wait if there was a man in the shop.
>
> It was after 4:00 in the afternoon and not long before the men would start arriving on their way home from work with their gasmask knapsacks they used to wear round their necks to carry their packed lunches – their 'bait'– and newspapers. John and I sat down on Bioletti's comfortable bus bench seats that the family had for the boys to sit on and read comics.
>
> We were behind two other boys in the queue when some men came in. Exasperated, John said to the two lads in front of us, 'Do you know, last week old man Bioletti cut off somebody's scalp completely, with his shaky hands. You could actually see the brains wobbling around like a dark grey blancmange inside the head. But he was alright 'cos he stuck the scalp back on with a sticking plaster.' The two boys left without a haircut and we got ours done before the rest of the men came in.

> I was nearly always in the same Sunday School and Bible Class with him. There was a motive! We had a Sunday School trip to the seaside resort of Southport, north of Liverpool, and in those days of single-sex schools, Sunday Schools were uni-sex so you got to sit with and talk to those strange creatures, girls!
>
> … We must have been 11 or 12 years old at least. 'Ma' Davies, the Sunday School teacher, got on about scribes and Pharisees and how they had treated Jesus. John Lennon got very annoyed about these scribes and Pharisees and said they must have been fascists. 'Ma' Davies blew her top and said that fascists were much, much worse than scribes or Pharisees.
>
> I also asked her if John was not right, just to support my mate, but I had no idea what fascists or scribes and Pharisees were in fact. We were hauled up in front of the Rev. Pryce Jones, rector of Woolton Church, who told us off in his lilting Welsh accent and then decided to cane us for causing trouble.

Music in the Fifties

● Use these pictures to describe the music and culture of teenagers in the Fifties.

A café

Record player, singles and LPs

Teddy boys

Buddy Holly and the Crickets

Lonnie Donegan

The Beatles

Learning Objectives

Children should:
- understand how and why the Beatles became so popular.
- research evidence of their success.

Background

Before they were discovered, the Beatles had spent seven formative years playing live. Their jeans and leather 'rocker' image was changed by their manager Brian Epstein. He got them to wear suits, stop smoking or swearing in public and bow at the end of a song. They were fortunate also in their producer, George Martin, who recognised the genius of the Lennon/McCartney combination and showed them how to enrich their sound in the studio. While Lennon and McCartney were the driving forces of the group, George Harrison and Ringo Starr were highly competent musicians and talented individuals and the dynamics between the four, and their irrepressible attitude, were clearly something special.

No other band has come close to the achievements of the Beatles. In 1963 their performance at the London Palladium was watched by 15 million and mobbed by hysterical fans. The press dubbed it 'Beatlemania'. They were the first British band to go straight to number 1 in the USA, where they performed to a record TV audience of 73 million. At one time they occupied the top five positions in the American singles chart. They were awarded MBEs for services to British industry in 1965. Liverpool is known throughout the world as the city the Beatles come from.

Starting Points	Main Activity	Simplified Activity	Extension Activity
L4 *'Early days of the Beatles'* Use photos, video or sound recording to introduce the first hits and TV appearances of the Beatles.	Ask the children to work in pairs to prepare their interview; one as Lennon and the other as interviewer. Ask some pairs to perform or record their interviews.	Give the children a copy of the sheet with information up to the end of 1963. Read the text with them and ask them to write an interview for this point in time.	Ask the children to carry out more of their own research on this period and to use it to add to their interview.
L5 *'Toppermost of the poppermost'* Talk about the type of evidence that measures the success of a band and give some clues to help with research.	Provide suitable resources and ask the children to find at least one piece of evidence for the seven headings. 'Other' is for anything falling outside these categories.	Give the children a sheet with examples of the Beatles' success and ask them to record them under the correct heading.	Ask the children to choose one of the events they have recorded and write a 1960s music magazine report on the event and the Beatles.
L6 *'The ingredients of success'* Talk about the reasons for the Beatles' success.	Provide A3-size paper; ask the children to cut out the pictures and create a page to record the factors discussed.	Give the children a list of sentences that they can match to each of the pictures and headings.	Ask the children to compare a favourite contemporary band and to compare them to the Beatles under the same headings.

Plenary

Choose an appropriate moment in the Beatles' history and hold a press conference role-play with four children to play the Beatles. You could add their manager and producer. The rest of the class are the journalists and should ask questions.

Early days of the Beatles

- Use these notes and the information on worksheets L2 and L3 to write an interview with John Lennon in 1964 about how he came to be famous. Role-play the interview with a partner.

Use the information below to help you answer the questions.

So John, when did you first become interested in music?

1956	John Lennon formed skiffle group, 'The Quarrymen'
1957	Playing at St Peter's Parish Church, Lennon was introduced to Paul McCartney, invites him to join the band
1958	McCartney's friend George Harrison joined on guitar
1959	Playing at the Casbah Club, the group met Pete Best
1960	Lennon asked friend Stuart Sutcliffe to join on bass guitar
	Hired a manager, Allen Williams
	Changed name to 'The Silver Beetles', then 'The Beatles'
	Did a tour of Scotland
	Drummer left, auditioned Pete Best
	Williams booked them on a two-month tour in Hamburg, Germany
	Aug–Oct: Played at the Indra Club – long hours, poor living conditions, but popular for energetic music
	Oct–Nov: Acclaim got them a place at a better club, the Kaiserkeller
	Dec: Returned to Liverpool
	Stuart stayed behind with girlfriend Astrid and quits the band
1961	Began playing at the Cavern Club
	Brian Epstein, a record shop owner, heard them and offered to be their manager – the group accepted
1962	**June:** Signed with Parlophone Records, part of EMI
	Producer, George Martin, got them to change drummer – Pete Best replaced with Ringo Starr
	Oct: First single Love Me Do got to number 17
1963	**Feb:** First album recorded Please Please Me
	Title single Please Please Me made number 1
	Further hits released: She Loves You, From Me to You, I Want to Hold Your Hand
	Oct: Played at London Palladium, term 'Beatlemania' used to describe hysteria of fans
	Nov: Royal Command Performance in front of the Queen Mother
	Dec: Released second album, With the Beatles

FOLENS HISTORY IN ACTION 6

Toppermost of the poppermost

John Lennon mockingly used the phrase 'toppermost of the poppermost' to describe their fame. The Beatles are generally recognised to be the greatest group in the history of pop music.

- Research and record examples of their success under these headings.

Hit singles	TV appearances
Album sales	Fans, popularity
Films	Awards
Fame abroad	Other

The ingredients of success

● Use these headings and pictures to explain why the Beatles were so successful.

Experience

Creative genius

Musical ability

Good manager

Good producer

Dynamics between individuals

Style and Image

Learning Objectives

Children should:
- be able to describe some of the changes in the Beatles' style and image during the Sixties.
- know some reasons for the break up of the Beatles at the end of the Sixties.

Background

The 1967 album, *Sergeant Pepper's Lonely Hearts Club Band*, put the Beatles at the forefront of the psychedelic movement that emerged first in rock music and went on to revolutionise film, literature and the visual arts. At this time there was a new sexual freedom and use of hallucinogens, marijuana and LSD among young people. Adherents believed that the drugs were mind-expanding and helped them to see truth or reality. Musicians experimented; they tried to recreate states of mind induced by drugs. Lennon's song *Lucy in the Sky with Diamonds* is a well-known example. It was inspired by a painting that his son brought home from school. The album, with its musical inventiveness and lyrical genius, is thought by many to be their best. It is obviously essential to point out to children that the Beatles and many others gave up using drugs when they realised the damage to their health and that many contemporaries were influenced by or enjoyed the new ideas in music, literature and art without taking any drugs.

Songs attributed to Lennon/McCartney were written by one or the other and fine-tuned together. The early songs were all on the theme of love. Lennon compositions for page 74 from the early Sixties include: *Please Please Me, Ask Me Why, Do You Want to Know a Secret?* (written for Cynthia Powell, shortly before they got married) and *A Hard Day's Night. Help* and *Nowhere Man* (1965) were the first Beatles' songs not to be about love and reflected how Lennon felt as a result of their lifestyle. Examples from the psychedelic period include, *Strawberry Fields Forever* (named after an orphanage in Woolton; John played in the grounds with friends as a child), *I am the Walrus* (basically nonsense words) or *Lucy in the Sky with Diamonds* (see above).

Starting Points	Main Activity	Simplified Activity	Extension Activity
L7 *'Changes in style'* If possible show a colour version of the Sergeant Pepper album cover. Talk about the psychedelic movement.	Ask the children to study the covers and discuss the differences in their own words. Ask individuals to describe how this relates to changes in culture before asking the class to write.	Ask the children to write a description of the appearance of the Beatles on each cover and the impression that it gives.	Ask the children to collect a number of images of the Beatles over the Sixties and use them to make a poster that shows their changing image.
L8 *'Changes in songwriting'* Select three Lennon compositions to show changes in style (see suggestions above). Discuss the terms 'mood' 'tempo' and 'theme' in relation to music.	Play each song a couple of times and allow time for children to discuss them and make notes. Discuss as a class how the songs reflect a change in style.	Ask the children to work with a partner who will help them to write down their observations about the songs.	Ask the children to write their own psychedelic-style verse. Choose an amusing subject or a first line to get them started.
L9 *'The break up of the Beatles'* Discuss the reasons that most bands break up eventually – the sorts of strain that the music industry creates. You may want to prepare more material on the break up.	Ask the children to read the texts. For the task they could work in pairs or groups, dividing the script between them. Provide more background material for a more detailed report.	Ask the children to choose one of the Beatles and to write an interview with that member about the break up.	Provide access to suitable resources and ask the children to research Lennon's alternative activities in the late Sixties. Ask them to report to the class and discuss how this might have contributed to the break up.

Plenary

Create a timeline for the Beatles and the Sixties. Give out cards with relevant events from the Sixties and ask the children to place them on the line.

Changes in style

● Use these two album covers to describe how the appearance and music of the Beatles changed during the Sixties.

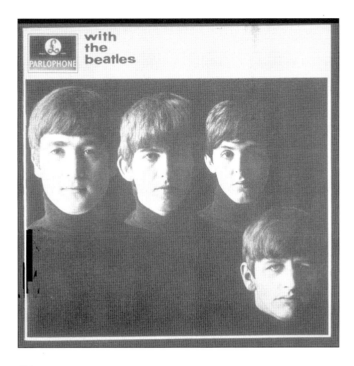

Changes:

_____

_____

_____

_____

_____

_____

_____

_____

_____

_____

_____

_____

Changes in songwriting

- Over the Sixties, the style of the Beatles' songs changed. Listen to three examples of songs written by John Lennon and fill in the table below.

	Early Sixties	Mid Sixties	Late Sixties
Title			
Mood			
Tempo			
Theme			

- Describe how the Beatle's songs changed over this period.

_____

_____

_____

_____

_____

_____

The break up of the Beatles

27 August 1967

Brian Epstein, the Beatles' manager, died. He was the person who had sorted out their arguments and handled all their money. After that the Beatles tried to handle their own finances but it was a disaster.

John

John was fed up of touring. He wanted to make a different kind of music with his new partner, Yoko Ono. He wanted the other Beatles to work with him and Yoko, but they weren't interested. John and Yoko made their own records.

George

He felt he could write songs too but he was only allowed to contribute two songs to each album. Since the Beatles went to India in 1968 he became very interested in Indian music and ideas, but John and Paul didn't want his songs on the albums.

Ringo

He was tired of just being the drummer. In August 1968 when the group were recording *The White Album* he got so fed up of the arguments, he walked out of the studio. He later returned.

Paul

He wanted his father-in-law, Lee Eastman, to be their new manager. The others voted against him for a manager called Allen Klein. Paul didn't like Klein. Klein hired Phil Spector, a producer, to work on the Beatles' songs and Paul felt that Spector was ruining their music.

10 April 1970

Paul announced publicly that he was not going to work with the Beatles anymore. He said there were too many differences between them and he preferred to be with his family. Until then the others had said in interviews that the Beatles would still work together, even if they made their own records as well. Now it was definitely over.

- Imagine it is 1970, after Paul's announcement, and you are a journalist. Use the information above (and more research of your own) to write a short TV or radio report about the break up of the Beatles. Include interviews with members of the group and your own comments on the reasons. Work with others to record or film your report.

John Lennon's Influence

Learning Objectives

> **Children should:**
> - evaluate Lennon's influence on society.
> - consider the most appropriate ways of commemorating Lennon.

Background

On the morning of 8 December, 1980, in New York City, a mentally disturbed fan, Mark David Chapman of Honolulu, asked for an autograph from Lennon, which he received. That evening, at 10.50pm, he was still there when Lennon and Ono were returning to their apartment building. As Lennon walked past him, Chapman called out "Mr Lennon," and fired five shots. Four of the bullets struck Lennon in the back. He yelled "I'm shot, I'm shot," and ran a few steps towards the building before collapsing in the entrance. He remained conscious as paramedics arrived, but died in hospital of cardiac arrest as a result of massive blood loss. Hundreds of people gathered in the street outside the apartment building, lit candles, laid down flowers near the gate and sang Lennon's best-known songs.

While the impact of the Beatles on pop music is huge and indisputable, it is more difficult to assess Lennon's impact on his times as an individual – an opportunity for children to make their own interpretation. He clearly struggled to overcome some of the psychological damage of his early life (his father leaving, being given away by his mother and, later, witnessing the death of his mother), and an addiction to drugs. He and Yoko were dedicated campaigners for peace. However, it was the music of the Beatles collectively that put him in the media spotlight and gave him the opportunity to influence. Also, assassination has given him a martyr status he would not otherwise have had.

Starting Points	Main Activity	Simplified Activity	Extension Activity
L10 *'Death of John Lennon'* Explain the events of Lennon's death. List words to describe typical reactions to an unexpected death (shocked, grief-stricken).	Ask the children to read the texts and look at the picture and to choose one or two words that best describe the reaction expressed in each one. Ask them to use the words to write news headlines.	Ask the children to look at the picture. Ask them to choose words to describe the feelings of the mourners, and then write a short news report to go with it.	Ask the children to write their own news report of the murder, combining facts and opinion.
L11 *'John Lennon's work for peace'* Talk about the way famous people have an opportunity to influence others and discuss some contemporary examples.	Read the texts with the children; discuss how the peace campaign and John and Yoko would benefit. Encourage the children to debate the two points of view before writing.	After the class discussion, ask the children to write their own point of view about Lennon's work for peace.	Ask the children to make a similar page for a famous person they know about today or in the recent past. Ask them to compare Lennon with that person.
L12 *'Remembering John Lennon'* Talk about the ways in which we remember famous people.	Ask the children to discuss the memorials in pairs and rank them in order of best to worst ways of remembering. Ask individuals to explain their choices.	Ask the children to rank the memorials in order of which they would most like to visit, and then write a sentence to explain why.	Ask the children to design their own John Lennon memorial and describe it, saying where it would be.
L13 *'Lennon's vision'* Play the song *Imagine*. Discuss its appeal and evidence of Buddhist thought to explain verse one.	Ask the children to listen to the lyrics and to offer explanations of meaning and whether these things might be achieved, before writing their own song.	Ask the children to describe the image that they have in their mind as they listen to the song and to produce an illustrated copy.	Ask the children to find examples of other songs Lennon wrote about peace.

Plenary

With the class, plan a biography of Lennon. Decide what the chapter headings should be and ask individuals to give a summary of the information they would put in each chapter.

Death of John Lennon

● Find words to describe the various reactions to the news of Lennon's death. Use them to write newspaper headlines.

"At first I didn't believe he was really dead," said Chris Backus, one of a thousand mourners ... 'When I realized it was true then – bang! – part of my childhood was gone forever."

The question asked over and over again was why – why had Chapman, a moody, unemployed amateur guitar player who lived and worked in the South before moving to Hawaii three years ago, killed a man he was said to have admired for fifteen years?

from Newsweek magazine
(22 December, 1980)

BBC News Online's entertainment correspondent, Tom Brook, was the first British radio reporter on the scene outside the Dakota apartment building in New York the night John Lennon died. From his vantage point in a telephone kiosk a few yards from where Lennon was killed, he filed live reports to BBC Radio 4's *Today Programme* bringing the first news of the former Beatle's death to a shocked British audience.

'Looking back, as a journalistic endeavour, reporting on Lennon's death was not hard in mechanical terms. All that was required of me was to describe the surreal scenes outside the Dakota.

What was far more challenging was keeping my own emotions in check.

I had grown up with Lennon's music. I was a fan and I suddenly realised that his passing was truly shocking news. It began to hit me just as hard as it did the fans outside the Dakota, and many of the radio listeners in Britain.'

'The night Lennon died' from BBC News at <u>www.bbcnews.com</u>

Words to describe reactions:

_____

_____

_____

John Lennon's work for peace

In 1964 fighting broke out between North Vietnam and the US army in South Vietnam. The North Vietnamese wanted to unite the country under a communist government and the Americans wanted to stop them. The war grew bigger and bigger and thousands of lives were lost on both sides. From 1967 people in America and Europe began to protest about the war. John Lennon was one of the many famous people who campaigned for peace.

The 'Bed-In'

For a week in May 1969 John and Yoko used their honeymoon to attract publicity for the peace campaign. They checked into hotels in Montreal, Canada and Amsterdam and invited the media to come to their room. They said they were protesting against violence. This original and humorous protest attracted a huge amount of attention. They recorded John's song *Give Peace a Chance* and this became the anthem for the campaigners.

Using the media

John and Yoko held many other art and music events, interviews, adverts, demonstrations and happenings. Most of these were in Canada in 1969. Their Plastic Ono Band played at a concert called 'Live Peace' in Toronto in September. Some writers think that John and  Yoko helped to change the way campaigners fought for peace because they tried to use newspapers and television to pass on their message, rather than rejecting the media.

Returning the MBE

The Beatles had all been presented with medals by the Queen for their contribution to industry. As a protest, John sent his medal back in November 1969. He wrote a letter to give his reasons; one of them was because he disagreed with the British government's support of the Vietnam war.

Some journalists were sympathetic to John Lennon and thought he was doing a good thing. Others were more cynical and said that John and Yoko were also getting a lot of publicity for themselves.

- Write two magazine reports of John's peace work, one from each point of view.

Remembering John Lennon

- Here are four ways in which John Lennon's life has been commemorated. For each one, explain why you think it is or isn't a good way to remember him.

---

15 March 2002

JOHN LENNON'S CHILDHOOD HOME COMES TO THE NATIONAL TRUST

The National Trust is delighted that Yoko Ono has announced that she has purchased John Lennon's childhood home, *Mendips*, Menlove Avenue, Liverpool, and that she is giving it to the Trust.

---

8 December 2000

[Yoko Ono has used] the 20th anniversary of Lennon's death to focus attention on the act of violence that led to her husband's death outside the Dakota.

She has devised a billboard which stands in Times Square, and in two other American cities, which relays the unsettling news that since Lennon was murdered, 676 000 other people have been killed by guns in the US.

'The night Lennon died' from BBC News at www.bbcnews.com

March 2002

In Liverpool the airport was re-named *Liverpool John Lennon airport* and adopted the words 'Above us only sky' (from Lennon's song *Imagine*) as its motto.

Strawberry Fields memorial

The memorial is a triangular piece of land in Central Park, New York. In the centre is a mosaic of inlaid stones, from countries all over the world. In the middle of the mosaic is the title of Lennon's song, *Imagine*. Along the borders of the triangular area are benches in memory of other individuals. Along a path toward the south-east, a plaque lists the nations which contributed to building the memorial.

Lennon's vision

- Listen to the song *Imagine*. In your own words, say how Lennon wanted the world to change.

_____

_____

_____

_____

_____

_____

- Are we nearer to, or further away from, what Lennon wanted? What do you think?

_____

_____

_____

_____

_____

_____

- Write your own song to convey your wish for the world.